HEIR OF SORROWS 2

The People's Prince

HEIR OF SORROWS 2

The People's Prince

by
SYLVIE KRIN

PRIVATE EYE · ANDRE DEUTSCH

Published in Great Britain
by Private Eye Productions Ltd.
6 Carlisle Street, London W1.,
in association with André Deutsch Ltd.,
105-106 Great Russell Street, London WC1.
© 1989 Pressdram Ltd.

Designed by Bridget Tisdall
Printed in England by
The Bath Press, Bath, Avon.
ISBN 0 233 98476 3

Chapter One

THE STORY SO FAR: Charles, feeling an increasing sense of isolation, has sought solace without his young bride in the highlands of his beloved Glen Campbell.

Now read on . . .

C HARLES watched the expert hands of his faithful ghillie McWheatcroft as he cast a glittering Roman Oyster fly into the running waters of the River Doon. For a moment it hovered as if held by invisible threads before striking the sparkling surface of the water as the silver bodies of the salmon swam towards the line.

"Yon's a guid 'un, laddie!" cried the Caledonian fisherman whom Charles had known since he was in short trousers. "Ye'll now be makkin' a cast of yer ain."

Charles waded deep into the swirling water in his thigh-length green rubber boots. It was here that he always felt that oneness with nature - what his friend and mentor Sir Laurens van der Post had called "the harmony of the wind and water singing to Man's inner soul".

Why then did he feel so different now? Why then, despite the jovial presence of McWheatcroft and his faithful long-haired Golden Wonder Retriever Sandy, was he so ill at ease?

With a heavy heart he cast his line and watched as it soared and then fell into a patch of nettles. The Scotsman cackled and took a dram of 1,000-year-old double malt Glen Elton whisky from his hip flask.

"It's a rare fush that dwulls in yon nettles, Yor Majesty," he quipped. "Ye've made a reet balls-up the noo."

Charles reddened. He had always felt the need to prove himself to McWheatcroft, just as he did with so many older, wiser men.

Clearly this trip was doomed to failure. It was not fish he craved, it was the company of fellow human beings. That evening he began the long drive back to Kensington Palace.

"DARLING! I'm home!" Charles threw his case and his tackle on to the Armand Hammer tiling of the breakfast room, but his words echoed in the vastness of the ancient palace.

Then his eye alighted on a hastily written note on a leaf from a Filofax in a childish scrawl that he knew only too well: "Gone shopping with Bunty and Georgie. May be late. See you next week. Ciao!"

Charles slumped disconsolately into an armchair. The need to talk to someone, anyone, even his brother Edward, was overwhelming. He picked up the phone and dialled. It was Edward's voice, but not one he could talk to:

"Hi! This is the Really Useful Prince! Ha ha . . . I'm at the Palace . . . Theatre, geddit? Ha ha ha. Don't call us, I'll call you, as we say in showbiz. Ha ha ha! You've been a great audience . . . My name's Prince Edward . . . Goodnight."

Charles hung up in disgust. The patois of the showbiz world had never appealed to his fastidious and sensitive nature. He tried a series of other numbers. His sister was in Africa. Andy was on active service. The Duchess of Fergiana was opening the London Book Fair. Even his mother was busy, entertaining the visiting Akond of Swat and the Anakonda.

But there was one person he had yet to try, the one person he knew would always be at home to him . . .

THE priceless Napley clock struck four with an expensive chime as the tiny gold figure of a lawyer with his hand outstretched emerged from a little silver door. The elegant butler, Grayson, laid a tea-tray of gin and scones before Charles and his grandmother.

"So nice to see you, dear," said Grayson. "Come to Granny for a little chatette, have we? Tea and sympathy?"

"That will do, Grayson," cut in his grandmother with mock firmness.

"Hark at her! Get you, ducky! Next time you get a fishbone stuck in your throat you can whistle . . . Ma'am," he added sarcastically.

The old Queen chuckled, and so did the Queen Mother.

Charles helped himself to a large gin and spread clotted Yorkshire cream over a slice of Madeira. He was beginning to feel at ease in the familiar, cosy badinage of Clarence House.

"Now why the long face, Charles?" asked the sympathetic old lady, as she poured herself a generous measure from the bottle of Gebler-

Davies Dutch Gin. "Do you want to talk about it? You can tell Granny."

But as he downed his second cup of gin, Charles's troubles seemed further away and his cares began to slide from his shoulders.

He thought of Diana out shopping. What did it matter? She was young, it was to be expected, and he had other sources of consolation. Music, Art - after all, his watercolour of the Temple of the Four Winds in Bangkok had been accepted as the official "Save the Seals" Christmas card . . . and this gin was terrifically . . . fantastically. . . what was the word?

As if reading his thoughts, the sweet old lady leant forward and emptied the rest of the bottle into his cup.

His granny seemed a long way away as she spoke, and slightly blurred, but Charles felt a sense of warmth and well-being enveloping him like the tartan blankets she had lovingly placed over him in her ancient shooting lodge at Glen Hoddle when he was just a bairn . . .

"D'you know what I would do if I were in your shoes, Charles, what I always do when I'm down in the dumps?"

There was a short pause as Charles waited expectantly for his grandmother's pearls of wisdom.

"I get out the Daimler and get Grayson to drive me up to Scotland for a spot of fly-fishing. There's nothing like it to take away your troubles."

Charles suddenly felt the cake turn to lead in his stomach, and Grayson's smiling face was transformed into a hideous mocking gargoyle . . .

Chapter Two

Prince Charles, Heir to the Throne, has been subjected to a vicious personal attack by former Conservative chairman Norman Tebbit . . .

A LIGHT drizzle sprinkled the burgeoning leaves of the limes elders and horse chestnuts that stood in stately groves like sentinels beside the ancient lichen-clad bulwarks of Kensington Palace.

Charles laid aside his priceless Melachrino cello and with a sigh switched on the video machine, as Diana had instructed him, to record the scenes of her opening the London Marathon.

And there she was, looking more beautiful than ever as she stood on a dais, her starting-pistol raised. Beneath her a teeming swarm of young scantily clad athletes limbered up for the gruelling ordeal that lay before them.

Bang! Suddenly they were running, rank upon rank, through the narrow streets of the city.

What was the point of it all, he wondered, so many people running - to what end? It was sort of . . . incredibly . . .

His thoughts tailed away as he stepped back, inadvertently plunging his foot through the polished rosewood belly of his cherished instrument.

That decided him. He would take Diana's advice and go to Italy. Only that morning she had said: "Why don't you go off somewhere on your own? You've got friends there. Give the Contessa a ring. You can do your painting thing . . ."

Yes, she was right. What was it that his friend and mentor Sir Laurens van der Post had said? - "Trees that are planted too near to one another will soon wither and die. We are often closest when we are furthest apart."

T HE WARM Italian sun rose in majesty behind the Byzantine splendour of Ribena, casting a purple glow on its ancient basilica. Charles dipped his brush into a glass of Chianti and carelessly dabbed a few strokes on to his new painting, *View From My Balcony*.

The light laughter of a young girl broke the silence.

"Scusi, signor," she said in broken English. "I hope I not disturb you."

Charles turned to find his hostess's daughter, the beautiful Contessissima di Lambretta, standing before him, her dark Latin eyes scanning his painting with a mixture of curiosity and appreciation.

"I did not know," she stammered. "You so clever man. Make the bella, bella pittura."

Charles stood up, coughing nervously.

"It's only a hobby, you know," he stammered. "It's sort of a relaxing thing."

"But is so good what you do. I can see it is the church, no? You know it was built by very famous Italian man - Giuseppe Gorgonzola."

Charles marvelled at her knowledge of art and Italian history. And how wonderful it was to find a young woman who truly appreciated his humble attempts at capturing a thing of beauty on canvas.

"One day," she went on, coyly fingering her shoulder-length Titian hair, "I love to come to London. So many things to do and see."

Charles put down his brushes and moved nearer to her. He could already picture the two of them together. He would show her the paintings at Windsor. They could visit Stonehenge at twilight and see the fountains at Frogmore. And in the evenings, perhaps, he would play to her on his violoncello, once it had been repaired. His mind raced with possibilities.

"When do you want to come? I mean, this is tremendous . . . exciting . . ."

"I think pretty soon," the Contessissima replied. "Is sales time in July, si? Plenty good clothes cheap. And then we all go Wembley see Michael Jackson. I love all his record. Especially this one called *Bad*."

A thick dark cloud passed across the sun and the beautiful springtime landscape turned a cold and bitter grey.

Chapter Three

Prince Charles, Heir to the Throne, is to meet Noboru Takeshita, the Prime Minister of Japan, on a State visit - at last a chance for him to play an effective role on the world stage . . .

CHARLES checked his Collins Goon Show Diary and there it was, underneath the amusing photograph of Sir Harry Secombe saying "Are you there, Min?" - the entry "Buddha 3.30pm, the old lighthouse", his personal code for his monthly meetings with his friend and mentor Sir Laurens van der Post.

Charles jauntily placed a deerstalker on his head and, throwing his Hussey highland cape around his shoulders, stepped lightly into the spring sunshine and headed for Suffolk.

"The East is a mystery even today. A mystery wrapped in a skein of silk impenetrable to the outsider and unknown to those who live there."

Charles nodded earnestly, trying to follow the wisdom of the Sage. As the old man talked, Charles's eye wandered around the room. How well he knew it! The row of shrunken heads from Mombasa, each with its own story to tell. The Masai masks fashioned from Topkapi hide gazing sightlessly from the walls. In the corner, an enormous stuffed rhino head presiding over it all like a household deity. And that smell! Charles thought it was the East and its unknowable, unthinkable, inscrutable . . . thingy.

And there, in the centre of the room, squatting on a hand-carved miniature wooden futon, was the venerable explorer himself, his long aesthetic fingers clasped around a delicate porcelain cup of the finest Hoo Hee tea. Charles waited for a pause and then burst out eagerly: "Yes, yes, but how should I approach him . . . this Japanese chap? It's tremendously important that I get it right. . . one hears these people take offence so easily."

In his mind Charles remembered all too clearly the incident in Beijing when his father had offended his Oriental hosts by describing them as "slitty-eyed Nips".

The old man gazed thoughtfully into his tea. "When the sun meets the moon, it is neither day nor night," he explained.

Charles could only concur as he watched the old man refill his cup from the twelfth-century Yoko Ono tea urn.

"But Mr Takeshia . . . I mean . . . what does one wear?"

Sir Laurens rose from his Lotus Capri position and crossed to the bamboo bookcase. He withdrew a dusty old tome, *Etiquette and the Orient* (1912), and handed it to his young protégé.

"Remember one thing, Charles. These people had invented chess when we were still running about in woad. It is a great opportunity for you to relive first hand the wisdom of this ancient civilisation that can teach us in the West so much."

Outside the mighty breakers broke upon the shingle and mingled with the unmistakable sound from the room next door of Ted Lowe saying: "This great snooker star, with only one frame to clinch the title for the fifth time . . ."

Sir Laurens bowed and left the room, muttering: "This leaves Terry requiring snookers." Charles wondered what on earth it could all mean . . .

I T WAS ALL prepared. The low, black lacquered Kurasawa table; the rice paper screens; the delicate slices of raw fish; Charles in his silken dragon kimono, specially tailored by Diana's friends the Emmanuels. Yes, he thought, there was no doubt about it. There was a strange peace, a sort of unifying unity about everything.

Sir Alan Fitztightly knocked discreetly and announced his guest. "Mr Take . . . Take . . . the Japanese gentleman is here to see you, Sir."

As he spoke, the energetic figure of Mr Takeshita in a Pietro Annigoni silk suit and crocodile-skin shoes entered the room.

"Delighted to make your acquaintance, Sir. Great palace you've got here. Love the guys' hats outside."

Charles was speechless. In confusion he bowed, ushering his guest to the tea-table and offering him a bowl of sweet-scented Pan Am tea.

"Not for me, thanks. I could use a straight J&B, no ice, gets you drunk quick. Boy, that was some journey."

Charles persevered. "Your Excellency. It is a very great honour for me to welcome a dweller of the land of the lotus blossom to my humble palace. May you treat this simple dwelling as . . ."

"Yeah, yeah, yeah . . . By the way, I got something for you and your good lady."

Takeshita clicked his fingers and a swarm of Sumo wrestlers rushed into the room carrying large cardboard boxes bearing the legend "Made in Japan. This Way Up".

Mr Takeshita ripped one of them open and turned to Charles. "We heard how much you like music, so here's something with kisses from Tokyo. The very latest 49-piece wall-to-wall Videorama Music Audio Enhancement Unit Centre. I don't have to say that everything's digital."

He paused to look at Charles's blank astonishment.

"You can get Rick Astley so loud you'll blast your neighbours out of the block."

Charles looked at the vast array of speakers and realised in a moment of enlightenment that they resembled nothing so much as the tower blocks around his beloved St Paul's.

Whither had fled the ancient visions of far-off lands? Gone, gone, gone . . .

Chapter Four

Charles seeks solace on the polo field with his old friend and manager Major Ferguson . . .

"THAT WAS a wonderful chukka, my boy. You certainly whacked the Nabob there!" The Major clapped Charles heartily on the back and, removing first his monogrammed polo shirt and then his khaki shorts, he stepped naked into the shower.

Charles shyly removed his own clothes and, wrapping himself in a towel, moved toward the open-plan shower unit in the clubroom of the East Grinstead Sports Ground.

Charles gingerly entered the shower, testing the water with an outstretched hand. The Major was already soaping himself down with Monica All-Over Shower Gel. Charles felt uncomfortable. It was all too much like being back in the steamy atmosphere of the Ribbentrop Block at Gordonstoun with Mr Waldheim supervising the younger boys after games.

"You look like you could do with toning up a bit," said the Major, eyeing his slender white figure disparagingly. "Mustn't let yourself go, that's what I always say, Sir."

He turned towards Charles, seeming to flaunt his tanned muscular limbs which gleamed brightly in the steaming water.

"Perhaps you're right," said Charles as he stood beneath the jet. "I have had this sort of slightly, sort of off-key feeling for some time."

"I know exactly what *you* need!" laughed the Major in his best barrack-room manner, winking at Charles with an exaggerated leer. "I know this little place, back of Oxford Street. A good tone-up and you'll come out feeling a million dollars."

Charles brightened at the thought of this massage treatment. He had no idea that the Major was interested, as he himself was, in alternative medicine. The idea struck him as a good one. A centre for homeopathic relaxation therapy. Yes! Sauna, acupuncture, osteopathy . . . all the things Sir Laurens had so strongly championed in their long talks by the fireside in The Lighthouse, the old sage's Suffolk hideaway.

Charles rubbed himself vigorously with a heavy Irish Derrytown towelling towel and thought of Sir Laurens's dictum on the wholeness of oriental healing: "The nut and the kernel are neither one nor two." It was a sort of body and soul, yin and yang, thing . . .

"**Y**OU'VE been a long time. What have you been talking about?" Diana was sitting lazily at the wheel of her emerald green Thyssen GTX-400. The stereo was blaring hits from an album by George Michael.

Charles winced, but the Major's face lit up as his eyes took in Diana's slim svelte young figure encased in the gleaming leather upholstery.

The Major gestured to Charles and said gruffly: "You go in the back, old boy. My gammy leg, you know. Can't get in there. Must have a bit of room to stretch the old feller."

With that he gave Diana a broad smile and clumsily fell into the front seat next to her. "Sorry, old girl!" he chortled, retrieving his balance by placing his hand on her thigh. "Whoops! No harm done."

Charles watched the Major's performance with disbelief and horror. His leg had seemed fine in the shower. He had always had the impression that the Major was a fit man.

As the car sped on its way, the Major turned to Charles, who was sitting cramped in the back with his polo stick digging into his ribs. "It's terribly sweet of you to drop me off in Wigmore Street. Are you sure it isn't out of your way?"

Diana turned down the volume. "Not at all. It's a pleasure," she said airily.

"It's certainly a pleasure for me, eh? What? Ha ha," he replied, placing a large hairy hand on her delicate knee.

Charles looked on aghast. He blushed a shade of puce at the thought that this man was now part of the Royal Family, *his* family. His mother would be appalled. But at least the Major was sound on some things - like this health therapy club he had advocated in the shower.

At last, after what seemed an age, the car drew smartly to a halt outside a seedy-looking brick building in a back street of Soho. A red neon light shone over a door marked "Walk straight up. Members Only".

With his leg seemingly restored to normal, the Major sprang from the car. As he did so an elderly woman with dyed blonde hair and scarlet lipstick greeted him with the cry: "Stand by your beds, girls. It's the galloping Major!"

Charles slumped, crushed by a sudden realisation of the truth. "I do apologise, my dear. I had no idea. How absolutely ghastly . . . and that place . . . I thought . . ."

Diana clearly hadn't heard a word he said. "What a sweet old gentleman he is. They don't make them like that anymore. So full of life. So experienced. One of the old school. He makes a girl feel she's really a woman. Come on, why don't you sit in the front? You look a real 'nana huddling there."

"No thanks," he replied faintly. "I'm perfectly happy, thank you."

Oh, if only . . . if only . . .

12

Chapter Five

Charles has been invited to open the new Tate Gallery in Liverpool, and he has decided to motor up with his wife . . .

"IT'S TERRIFICALLY exciting what's going on in Liverpool. It's really a tremendous example of urban renewal." Charles manoeuvred the Frascati coupé (a present from King Ahs-ol of the Trucial States) into the fast lane, and all eight litres fired with the power of a turbo jet.

"Yup. Yup. Yup," Diana agreed, enthusiasm filling her voice. "Liverpool's t'rrific. All that history."

They sped through the English countryside, now at its most resplendent in the finery of early June. Emerald lushness stretched to the horizon, spattered with the first creamy white buds of hawthorn.

The Tate Gallery. How appropriate, Charles thought. The home of all those wonderful, terrifically evocative Constables like *The Mill at Trelford* where that chap in the red waistcoat was so English, so terrifically . . . He recalled his very first art lesson with the former president of the Royal Academy, Sir Hugh Casson, that venerable master of the brush. He had asked him how you painted clouds with watercolour.

"Leave gaps, Sir. Let the paper tell the story." There had been so much to learn.

His wife switched cassettes in the car stereo, a MikkiRuni in-vehicle entertainment centre given to the couple by the Emperor Hirohito himself. A snatch of something more melodic than normal filled the car. It reminded him of his schooldays at Gordonstoun. "If there's anything that you want . . ." He found himself tapping the steering wheel rhythmically. There was a lot to be said for this new music, after all. He smiled. To his surprise, he was enjoying his trip. Yes, it all seemed to be going terribly well.

"AND THIS is called *Trapezium Three*." Charles stared uncomfortably while the young director, Antoine de Rushton, pointed to what at first sight seemed to Charles to be a skip filled with earth. He had been prepared for this by Sir Hugh, who had told him that the Tate had purchased many new works like this one by the young Glaswegian sculptor Delwyn Swingewood.

"Oh, yes. Yes indeed." Charles tried to hide his distaste. "I see. How very. . . very. . ." What was he meant to say?

"The artist is making a statement, Sir, about urban renewal. His choice of the yellow skip is a witty reference to an earlier work called *Trapezium Two*," said the director, adjusting his bowtie with a flourish.

Charles tried hard to appear enthusiastic. After all, he had always said how important it was to encourage new talent. How had Sir Laurens, his old friend and mentor, put it? "The crescent new moon always comes as a surprise. But as it grows old and full we see it with familiar eyes."

Charles moved towards another exhibit, entitled *Poll Tax*, which was a large plank of wood painted red.

"Aren't there any sort of pictures, you know, sort of Constables?" he queried.

"Very amusing, Sir. Ha ha ha . . ." The group of bearded officials laughed in unison. He seemed to have made a joke. Was Diana laughing?

14

He looked for her but, as so often, she was nowhere to be found. Perhaps she was lingering over the mobiles - there was one, he noted, called *Flying Penis* - or had he imagined it? Gritting his teeth, he moved on. Only another 200 exhibits . . .

At last it was over. Alderman Scousegit thanked Charles profusely and saw him to his car where Diana was already sitting.

"Wasn't it terrible?" Charles said as he pulled away from the kerb. "I'm never going there again. All that modern rubbish. I can't understand what people see in it. Don't you agree?"

Diana brushed a lock of blonde hair from her cheek and pulled a large plastic bag from under the seat.

"No, I thought it was great," she enthused.

"You mean the gallery . . . the Tate?"

"No, silly. The Cavern Club. Where d'you think I've been while you've been dragging round all that arty stuff?"

She opened a bag emblazoned with the legend "FAB FOUR OFFICIAL SOUVENIR", pulled out a John Lennon black leather cap and placed it coquettishly on her head.

"And I've got something for you, too," she added with a hint of a giggle.

"Oh, how generous," Charles replied tentatively with a sinking feeling in his heart.

Diana dipped into her bag of memorabilia and extracted a large plastic guitar printed with the words "John, Paul, George and Ringo. Made in Taiwan". Lurid colour pictures of the young mop-haired quartet were displayed on the back of the instrument.

Diana strummed it amateurishly and sang "She loves you, yah, yah, yah" in a girlish voice.

A distant clap of thunder rolled over the Wiltshire hills and ahead a black cloud loomed. Suddenly another Beatles lyric came into his mind - "Will you still need me, will you still feed me, when I'm sixty-four?"

There could be no answer. Not now, perhaps not ever.

Chapter Six

Charles and his young wife Diana are attending the annual Prince's Trust Concert . . .

"I WANNA love your body now. Ooh, yeah, baby." The sound, amplified a million times, pulsated through the Albert Hall and thousands of young fans clapped and screamed in time to the gyrating figures of Rik 'n' Sam, the blonde girl duo who were taking the charts by storm. In the Royal Box Charles fiddled uncomfortably with his programme. Everybody around him seemed to be enjoying themselves, including Diana. Even Sir Alan Fitztightly, standing discreetly by the door, tapped the toe of his patent leather shoe and nodded his head in an agreeable fashion.

"Yubba! Yubba! Yubba!" Sir Alan smiled at Charles. "Awfully good, Sir, don't you think, Sir?"

Diana, standing on a seat with her friends Bunty Coker and Georgie Cavendish, playfully poured a plastic beaker of Cherrycide-Cola over his head. "Wake up, Grandad!" she cried. "This is your big day, remember?"

Yes, how right she was, he thought, as Georgie disappeared over the edge of the box into the swaying throng below. Indeed it was his day, and it would be wrong to judge the young people from what he could see on the stage.

By now another group had appeared, "The Cee-Dees", four fresh-faced youngsters in baggy box-shouldered jackets singing an *a cappella* version of "Too Late To Love, Too Soon To Cry". They might seem to lack the obvious graces but, as Sir Laurens van der Post had so often observed, "From the humble maggot emerges the divine bluebottle."

It was one of his mentor's more obscure *aperçus* which Charles found difficult to grasp. Still, it was some sort of appearance and reality thing. Like these singers who, he had read so often in Diana's magazines, were so interested in South Africa, nuclear disarmament and that sort of thing.

Afterwards he felt sure they would find much to talk about despite their different backgrounds. He looked at his watch. Only another four hours to go. His reverie was broken by Diana screaming, "Oh God! I can't believe it! It's The Sherpas . . ."

"BLACK PEPPER, Signori? Fantastico. A little sexy salad for a Bella Principessa." The rotund figure of Luigi, proud proprietor of Mr Wong's Malaysian Ribhouse and Carvery, hovered around the large table. It had been Charles's idea to hold the dinner in the more informal surroundings of this fashionable King's Road eaterie.

Charles turned to the man sitting next to him.

"And which one are you?" he asked politely as he cut himself a modest slice of stir-fried sweet 'n' sour Chicago pizza.

His dinner companion looked blank.

"Yeah. Right. I agree."

Charles nodded furiously. "I thought you were terribly good this afternoon. I'm tremendously impressed by the way everyone gets together to do their bit for, you know, Nelson Mandela."

"Nelson who? I don't know his stuff."

"Or the Sharpeville Six?"

"Is that an American band? Like the Jackson Five?"

Charles persisted, desperately hoping to strike a chord with this young performer who was wearing mirrored Boesky shades even though the table was lit only by a guttering candle.

"I'm very involved in Greenpeace."

"Are you? Are you the lead singer? Take my advice, stick to sixties material, mate, old Motown stuff, and you can't go wrong. We sold ten million of the Buicks' 'Sha La La'. We cleaned up on that one."

From the far end of the table came a shout of raucous laughter as Charlie Ricketson-Smythe bent over Diana, brandishing the giant pepperpot in a suggestive manner. Luigi replenished their glasses with flaming sambucca and the sweet trolley was wheeled on by his elderly mother, Signora Kray.

"Dolce, para tutti, bitte." Charles was not to be defeated by the sweet trolley or anything else. "Just a black coffee, please. As I was saying" - he drew his seat closer to the young man - "there is this wonderful Baron Thyssen collection that I'm trying to get."

"I've given up collecting albums. I collect vintage cars. I wrote one off the other day - 1924 Ridley worth three-quarters of a million. I hit a tree on the M25."

Reluctantly Charles gave up and sought solace in his sambucca. Unfortunately, amidst the hullabaloo of Georgie Cavendish shoving profiteroles down Ricketson-Smythe's trousers, Charles had not noticed that the supper liqueur had been set alight by the solicitous hand of Signora Kray. "Aaargh!" he cried, as the flame singed his lips and the pain shot through his head like a laser beam.

A round of applause, led by Diana, greeted his accident.

"Oh look! Charles is pretending to be a fire-eater. Everybody watch!"

Charles smiled weakly and wished he were 10,000 miles away. In the Kalahari, in one of the threatened rainforests, even in Soweto. Anywhere but here . . .

Chapter Seven

It is Wimbledon fortnight and as usual Princess Diana has taken the Duchess Fergiana to their seats in the Royal Box for the men's semi-finals . . .

"QUIET PLEASE!" The umpire's mellow tones settled the buzz of electricity around the Centre Court as the spectators focused their attention on the tall young German serving with three break points in the second set.

"Isn't Krautmann a hunk?" Fergiana giggled to Diana. "Look at those muscular thighs." She took another huge mouthful of strawberries drenched in dairy cream.

Thwok! "Out. Second service."

The tall German threw his racket at one of the ballboys, catching him a glancing blow on the head. "You haf got to be joking, you blind jerk!" The crowd booed its disapproval at the German's latest tantrum,

but in the Royal Box the voice of Charlie Ricketson-Smythe could be clearly heard expressing a more favourable opinion.

"Good old Fritz!"

Everybody laughed, especially Georgie Cavendish, who was on her tenth Pimms.

"New balls please." Fergiana dug Diana playfully in the ribs. "We could do with some of those," she said in a voice that carried on the summer air. The tall German looked up at the Royal Box and gave a punched fist salute.

"Hello, pretty ones! This vun is for you!" he cried, immediately serving an ace down the centre line. "Game to Krautmann. Krautmann leads Ozbore two sets to love . . ."

THE SLEAK Austin Mitchell coupé sped effortlessly through the traffic behind the police escort. Diana and Fergiana sat comfortably in the back watching replays of themselves on the car video.

Fergiana finished a triple Dolcevita Nut and Banana Sundae. "I thought you said Charles was coming to look at the painting. Everybody loves it. It's such a laugh having your picture done by a real artist."

Diana picked up the car phone. "I'll tell him to come. What time?"

Georgie Cavendish at the wheel swerved to avoid a red light, knocking an elderly man off his bicycle.

"Look where you're going, Grandpa!" yelled Ricketson-Smythe

through the open window, throwing a half-empty punnet of strawberries at his recumbent form. "Bloody idiot. Could have had us all killed."

"Hello. Hello." It was Charles. "Is that you, Diana?"

"Yah. Listen, we're all going to Fergie's pad to see the new painting. You're the expert, so you've got to be there. 8.00 and bring a bottle. Must dash."

THE PAINTING was hung in the place of honour above the television in the drawing room at Thaxted Lodge. Overhead the jets from Heathrow rumbled reassuringly as Charles picked his way through the piles of discarded Dire Straits CDs and back numbers of *Harper's & Queen*. Already there were noticeable burns in the deep pile of the avocado nylon Weidenfeld carpet.

"What do you think, Rembrandt?" joked Fergiana, gesturing towards Bryan Nogue's masterpiece, *The Duke and Duchess of York, 1988*.

Charles stared in acute embarrassment. In truth, he had not even recognised his brother and sister-in-law, but he felt compelled to comment since the whole room was waiting for his opinion.

"Er . . . it's . . . fantastically . . . terrifically . . . interesting . . . different . . . the brushwork is . . . er . . . colours, you know." His voice faded. How would his old friend and mentor Sir Laurens van der Post have coped? "Sometimes a man must remain silent in order to speak." Yes, how very true that was.

Fortunately Concorde boomed overhead, putting an end to Charles's dilemma and allowing Diana a chance to give her view.

"Well, I think it's brill! In fact I want one and we're going for our first sitting Tuesday, Wednesday, Thursday next week. Wear something casual, like your naval uniform."

Charles shuddered as Georgie Cavendish woke up with a gale of laughter and asked "Who's winning?"

"But," Charles stuttered, "you can't be serious. Our family has them done by Signor Pellegrino, he does Mother and everyone. This is all very well but . . . "

Diana ignored him and switched on the television beneath the portrait. As the camera focused on an Australian figure swearing at an umpire Charles felt his sense of discomfort increase.

"Isn't it appalling? The way these people go on nowadays. Even Wimbledon. It used to be so English, so gentlemanly, so . . . and now some young people even applaud this sort of behaviour."

As he spoke, the camera cut away to the Royal Box where his wife, Fergiana and their friends could clearly be seen cheering the Australian as he pushed the elderly umpire off the top of his ladder and emptied a bottle of Rees-Mogg's Olde Englishe Lemon Barley Water over his bald head.

Charles sighed. It seemed like game, set and match to this brave new world in which he felt so out of place . . .

Chapter Eight

The popular singer Michael Jackson has arrived in Britain for his sell-out tour. Charles has been dragged to see him by his young wife, who now wishes to go again . . .

"**F**OR once I'm really going to put my foot down." Charles got up from the breakfast table and strode purposefully to the french windows. In the park outside Kensington House a light drizzle was falling on a group of Japanese tourists photographing each other. Charles clasped his hands behind his back and tapped his foot in irritation. She had never seen him like this before. Touchy and stubborn.

"I've done my fair share of listening to chaps screaming at one in Wembley and so forth, including this Jackson man dressed up in his leather. No, Diana. It really won't do."

There was clearly no point in arguing with him.

"OK. Forget it. I didn't want to go anyway," she pouted. "There's no need to get your knickers in a twist, all right?" She turned away from him, nibbling on a crisp chocolate croissant from Madame Rosenthal's Viennese Patisserie in nearby Seagrove Street as she listened to Jackson's "Dirty Diana" on her Walkman.

Charles walked back to the table and poured himself a cup of finest Nagorno-Karabakh tea.

"You see, darling, it's all very well spending one's time dancing about to this music, but we don't want people to think we're frivolous in some way." Charles took a sip and stared deep into the bottom of the handpainted Finknottle teacup. "So many people are doing so many exciting things. In my job I have to be there, give a lead, you know what I mean. Not everything Papa says is rubbish. Sometimes in his blunt sort of way he really, you know . . ."

Diana dabbed her rose-pink lips with her napkin. To his surprise, she replied:

"Yah. Yah. I see what you mean. Yah. Perhaps you're right."

Charles gave her a triumphant smile. This firm approach really was working. That was something his father had said: "If you're having trouble with a filly, give her a touch of the whip."

Charles was even more delighted when later on that day he found Diana poring over a coloured brochure entitled *Post-Modernist Architecture in Milton Keynes.*

"Just look at these, Charles. Aren't they fab? Look at this one, it's got pillars on the front."

Charles sat down beside her on the large Betjeman sofa that dominated the drawing room.

"Yes, you see it's a sort of classical pastiche incorporating older elements, so it's accessible to real people in their real lives."

As he explained the simple architectural terms to his young wife, he felt a surge of pride well up inside him. He knew now how his own mentor must feel when he sat devotedly at his feet. How had Sir Laurens put it? "The old oak passes on its wisdom to the acorn." How terribly profound that was!

"I'd love to see it. How about going this week? Thursday evening?"

Charles blinked with amazement.

"You really mean it?"

"Yah. Absolutely."

"Right. I'll cancel my painting lesson with Sir Hugh. I'm sure he won't mind . . ."

I T WAS quite extraordinary. In the heart of Buckinghamshire there was this vibrant city, a real live centre of new ideas and aspirations. He gazed in wonder at the new Christopher Booker Technology Pavilion in smoked glass and aluminium. And there next to it, in exciting contrast, was the Gavin Stamp Heritage Centre in red brick with Dutch gabling and York stone cladding. And there! The post office, the work of Arno Goldfarb, an American architect Charles had met on his visit to Philadelphia. How original to have left out all the windows.

But what impressed him most of all were the crowds of happy

young people thronging the streets in huge numbers. They all appeared to be smiling, and also, he observed, to be all going in the same direction. How extraordinary! Was there any significance in the fact that they all wore T-shirts with the legend "BAD" on them? Was it a comment on something? He would have to ask Diana.

She had run ahead excitedly when, quite by chance, she had recognised the figures of Bunty Coker, Charlie Ricketson-Smythe and Georgie Cavendish struggling with a 12-litre bottle of Lambretta sparkling wine just ahead of them.

What an incredible coincidence, Charles thought. Could they all be interested in architecture?

Suddenly, as they turned a corner by the Alan Sugar Sports Complex, an enormous stadium loomed above them.

"Look, darling, we must go in here. I bet it's really interesting!" cried Diana gleefully.

As his wife spoke, multi-coloured searchlights lit up the sky and a pounding beat deafened all those within earshot.

"What is it?" Charles asked incredulously. "Some sort of *son et lumière*?"

The disembodied voice of an announcer behind the high concrete walls answered his question in a transatlantic accent.

"Ladies and gentlemen - tonight, here at the Milton Keynes Bowl, the legend to end all legends! Put your hands together for . . ."

His last words were just audible as a massive scream swelled into the night air.

"Mr Michael Jackson! And he's BAD!!"

Charles stopped dead in his tracks.

Yes, it was bad. Frightfully bad. Really very, very bad indeed . . .

Chapter Nine

Charles feels listless as the dullest summer in years drags on into weary August . . .

CHARLES rinsed his paintbrush furiously in a jar of greyish water and stared disconsolately at his latest effort, entitled *The Villa Frescobaldi at Sunset*. No. No. No. It simply wouldn't do. That house bit behind the olive groves, it didn't look like that at all. And the sun, a deep blood orange when he had seen it in Italy, had gone a sort of dirty brown colour and got mixed up in the sky around it.

His failure to capture the romantic setting of the Contessa's Florentine villa in the Lamborghini Hills mirrored his present mood. Walking to the window, Charles watched as yet another grey day glowered at him through the leaded panes of his makeshift studio.

There was a faint drizzle in the air. He sighed into a silence broken only by the dull thud from the room below of his wife's latest CD - *LoveSexy* by someone all too ironically called Prince. Would that she listened to him with as much enthusiasm . . .

He decided to abandon the watercolour on his easel and looked at the eighteenth century Halpern carriage clock that stood on the mantelpiece next to the silver polo trophies. Not that there had been many of those to add to his collection recently. 4.30pm. Three hours until dinner with the British Diary Manufacturers Association, of which he had been elected the honorary president.

Was it him, or was it stuffy in the room?

He opened the window and was met by a blast of rain that drenched the front of his artist's smock, a gift from the Irish Tourist Board, decorated with shamrocks and the legend "Good luck from the Emerald Isle".

Instinctively, Charles walked to the telephone and dialled the familiar number. "Hullo, Sir Laurens. It's me. Charles . . . er . . . you know . . . Windsor . . . Can you spare a moment?"

THEIR FEET crunched into the shingle in unison as the heavy waves pounded the shore. The old man bent into the wind and listened as Charles poured out his heart.

"You see, everyone's got their own sort of thing. Diana and this music . . . Fergie, well you know, this baby . . . Anne's always busy doing good works . . . Grandma down the East End the other day even at her age . . . terrific, really, marvellous."

The words were carried away on the salty breeze as gulls screeched high above them. Sir Laurens nodded.

"And you?"

Charles's silence spoke volumes as the two continued to walk back to The Lighthouse, the guru's coastal retreat. Suddenly the white-haired figure bent down and picked up two pebbles, one large and one small.

"We are like these stones," he explained in his familiar reassuring tones. "In life we must be both, the big and the small stone."

Charles saw at once the brilliance of the metaphor. It was a kind of symbol. He would have to be someone's big stone. But who would be the small one?

CHARLES poked his head round the stage door of the Palace Theatre in the heart of London and was greeted by a small man with a moustache and a gold earring.

"Edward? You mean Her Majesty, dear. She's second floor, third door on the right. Expecting you, is she?"

Charles explained that it was an impromptu visit, and the man in the tartan shirt waved a desultory hand in the direction of Edward's office.

His brother was sitting at a desk with his feet up, reading an old copy of *The Stage*. The room was strangely still. Charles had expected all the hustle and bustle of the theatrical whirl. There was not so much as a sound. Charles coughed.

On seeing who it was, Edward sprang to his feet and picked up the phone.

"Get me Gielgud on red. He's at the Phoenix with Sir Peter and Trevor. Maggie Smith is still on hold - right. Hi, Maggie baby, talk to you later - great perf, no honestly, you were fab - Hal Prince? Yeah, dinner for two at DonRevi's and Tony Sher's joining us for coffee . . ."

He placed his hand over the mouthpiece and whispered: "Take a seat, bro'. With you in a sec."

He continued to talk animatedly into the receiver.

"Am I in to Harold Pinter? No way, José! Ayckbourn? I've got a window at three next Tuesday - maybe! Confirm the New York trip for Monday, and I'll look at the sets for *Dreamcoat* at five. Tell Maria the costumes are too too divine - love you. Ciao!"

He dropped the instrument into its cradle and extended a hand to his brother.

"Sorry about that. You know how it is in this biz - go-go-go!"

Charles sat on a box marked "Les Mis. NY". Yes, of course he understood, although in truth he had little idea what Edward was talking about.

His brother began energetically shifting piles of scripts around his desk.

"So what brings you to the roar of the greasepaint and the smell of the crowd, as we say. Ha ha ha . . . Don't tell me Di wants some comps for *Phantom*? She's only seen it eight times, ha ha ha . . ."

Charles searched for an opening. On the way he had been so sure that, as Edward's elder brother, he could be the Big Stone of the fable.

"I just wanted to check, you know, everything was . . . er . . . you know . . . anything you wanted to talk about. . ."

Edward looked up.

"Sorry? Song here caught my eye. I think I can make it work."

"I was just wondering . . ." Charles went on.

The phone rang. Edward threw up his hands apologetically.

"It'll be my call from LA. Spielberg tends to ring in about now . . ."

Charles realised it was hopeless. His brother, who clearly had no need of a sympathetic older ear, was talking.

"That's six. Three white, no sugar. One black with a dash. And some Jaffa Cakes. Right!"

He strode purposefully towards the door, counting out some ten-pence pieces in his hand.

"Love you and leave you, Charlie boy. When you gotta go . . . you gotta go. Big production meeting Andrew . . . Sarah . . . every-one . . ."

And with that he was gone, leaving Charles alone in the strangely empty office high above the hum of London's busy traffic.

Charles put his head in his hands. He was still a small stone; his dreams of a bigger part in the drama of his family, let alone life, were still to be unrealised . . .

Chapter Ten

For months the Family had been talking of nothing but Fergiana's baby. And now at last it had arrived . . .

THE HOUSE seemed strangely silent in the dull, heavy August afternoon. Dog days. The trees themselves were limp and tired, the grass beneath the window parched and brown. Even the bees seemed to have given up.

Perhaps it was this greenhouse effect that his environmental friend, Jonathan Merryweather, had told him about, or perhaps it was merely that limbo that Sir Laurens so often mentioned that preceded new life.

Yes! That must be it. Yes. Yes. A sort of death before birth thing. It was fantastic really how everything was part of a sort of pattern. How had the old sage put it on one of their many walks along the shingle at Sizewell-on-Sea? "The moment when the tide is furthest out is the moment when it is furthest in."

Charles opened the french windows and walked into the Mogul garden designed by his talented cousin David Hicks.

He sat in the miniature replica of the Taj Mahal and stared at his reflection in the lake. How he had changed since he was Andrew's age! Was his younger brother - so wild, so carefree - really ready for the great responsibility that was fatherhood?

Charles was not sure but he remembered his own twenties when he himself had thrown caution to the wind. There had been wild parties, vintage cars, beautiful models, creeping along darkened passages to secret trysts, days rolling into nights and never a care for tomorrow . . .

Dropping a pebble into the water he watched the ripples distort his face and felt sure that his brother too, in his turn, was on the verge of a new kind of maturity.

"Ripeness is it." Who said that? He would ask Sir Alan Fitztightly to look it up.

OUTSIDE the grey façade of St Bupa's maternity hospital huge crowds of wellwishers waved Union Jacks and sang "For he's a jolly good fellow!" Already Charles felt buoyed up on a wave of jubilation as he made his way along the corridor towards the exclusive Sainsbury Wing.

Yes, it was the beginning of a whole new relationship between him and his brother. In his mind's eye he could see Andrew and himself reading stories to the child by the fireside. Perhaps she would like one of his own offerings, *The Old Bore of Glen Morangie*. And then drawing lessons up at Balmoral with Sir Hugh?

Yes . . . His pace quickened as he approached a door marked "Princess Fergiana", from behind which came the unmistakable sound of loud music mixed with high-pitched laughter.

Had he come to the wrong room? But then the door burst open and the familiar figures of Bunty Coker and Georgie Cavendish spilled into the corridor.

"Room for a little one in there," giggled Georgie, clutching a jeroboam of the Alain Prost vintage champagne.

"You're just in time for the christening," added Bunty.

Charles stepped into the room and was transfixed by the scene that greeted him.

On the bed was the Duchess, surrounded by huge bouquets of exotic orchids and blossoms. Sharing the bed was the comatose figure of Rupert Ricketson-Smythe, his cricket sweater wrapped around his head. In a corner was a steel band, led by a dreadlocked man whose T-shirt proclaimed him to be "Sir Roy Kerridge".

Their attempt to play "Happy Birthday, however, was somewhat thwarted by the 200 watt Rees-Mogg "speakers blasting out "He Doesn't Want Me" from *Phantom of the Opera*.

Diana was watching a video of herself on the television with a staff nurse and a large male auxiliary who was finishing a huge slice of gin-flavoured strawberry gateau, a present from the Queen Mother.

And there in the middle was Andrew, the proud father, his face flushed with the excitement of his new role. He was holding the baby upside down, pouring champagne over its head and shouting: "I name thish ship HMS *Shtringfellow*!"

Charles quietly closed the door and retraced his steps, sadly clutching the wilting bunch of mixed chrysanthemums that he had picked himself from his garden.

"Aren't you staying, Sir? I hear there's a great party going on," said the cheery policeman at the door.

"No . . . no . . . I don't think so . . ." he said, quietly going out into the night . . .

Chapter Eleven

Charles has taken his reluctant young wife for a traditional holiday at Balmoral, where the Duchess Fergiana is holding court with her new baby, Princess Beatrice . . .

THE MISTS swirled over the summit of Ben Loon, the mighty crag that towered high over the heather-strewn moorland of Glen Campbell. A huge eagle soared above, its wings spread majestically against the grey-blue of the late afternoon Highland sky.

Seated at his easel, Charles could contemplate life's disappointments with equanimity. His delight, for example, when his brother had named his daughter after the wonderful heroine in Dante Alighieri's masterpiece had turned to dust when Andrew had looked blank and told him that "Beatrice" was Georgie Cavendish's favourite nightclub in Verbier. Somehow it was all part of the Divine Comedy . . .

In the distance Charles could hear the faint blasting of guns as his father's party celebrated the opening of the quail season.

"You bloody idiot!" the Duke could be heard yelling. "Don't you know that sheep are out of season?"

Charles breathed a sigh and contemplated his half-finished watercolour, provisionally entitled *Ben Loon at Sunset*. Should he put in the eagle? He was not sure he could manage it.

Still, it was wonderful to spend a day on his own up here in the untamed wilderness. How had Sir Laurens put it? "An eagle may soar above a mountain, but a mountain may not soar above an eagle." How true that was - but how few people ever stopped long enough to sort of empathise as it were with nature's deep thingy . . .

He would have to say as much to the others when they came to collect him in the Queen's new DaniLaru Range Rover, a present from His Highness King Juan Fortharōd of Majorca.

Talking of which, where on earth had they got to? They had dropped him off in the morning on the way to a shopping expedition in nearby Auchtermuchty, and Diana had promised faithfully that they would be back at teatime.

Charles glanced at his Lonrho chronometer, whose waterproof face was already spotted with rain. It was a quarter to six. He looked up as dark clouds raced across the moorland, ominous like a huge black curtain enveloping the scene and its lone inhabitant.

He hurriedly packed up his easel, pulled his Kagool firmly down over his kilt (the MacHackey tartan favoured by all the Royal Family) and began to walk. He would be bound to meet them along the way . . .

THE "Tiny Rowland" German hunting clock struck eleven as the bedraggled figure of Charles pushed his way into the cosy atmosphere of the Balmoral drawing room.

A familiar scene greeted his weary eyes: the Queen playing Scrabble by the fireside with her devoted corgi "Sir Alastair"; the Duke of Edinburgh plucking a brace of quail and throwing the feathers on to the fire; his grandmother, her face flushed and merry, feeding the infant Princess Beatrice from a strangely coloured milk bottle that seemed in the half-light to bear the imprint "Gordons".

And there, giggling on the sofa, the Duchess Fergiana and his wife Diana, watching the video of a "Seal Aid" concert that they had been to the previous week.

"Hello, everyone," Charles began, wringing out his Fairclough sweater and hanging it to dry in front of the fire. "What happened to you lot?" There was just a hint of irritation in his voice. "You were meant to pick me up hours ago. I had to walk fifteen miles in the pouring rain."

"So what? Do you some good!" exclaimed his father, pulling out the entrails from the now-balding quail and throwing them to Sir Alastair.

"I'm really sorry, Charles," interposed Diana, "but Fergiana had to get back to feed Bee-Bee and you know there just wasn't time. Anyway, we thought you'd enjoy it - the rain and the walk and being on your own. I mean, that's why we left Majorca early, isn't it?"

Charles could find no answer to that, standing steaming in the middle of the family gathering. And perhaps he had enjoyed it after all. One must be positive . . .

"Sit down and belt up! Your mother's trying to play Scrabble."

The sharp tones of the Duke woke the baby, who immediately began to cry, wailing disconsolately with a barely understood misery.

Charles sometimes wished that he could express himself as freely . . .

Chapter Twelve

Charles and Diana are planning a night out together at the cinema, but fate, in the form of a mysterious letter, rules otherwise . . .

CHARLES looked down at his Butoni patent leather pumps and adjusted his black bow-tie in the ornate gilded Sabatini mirror. "Are you ready, darling?" he called. At the other end of the bedroom his beautiful young wife Diana was placing her svelte form in a shimmering chiffon and shot silk off-the-shoulder evening gown by her close friend and designer, Baz Bamigboye.

"Couple of ticks, darling. Could you be absolutely sweet and zip me up?"

Charles moved across the room, enthusiastically delighted at his wife's obvious excitement at the evening ahead. It had been so long since they had been out à *deux* and now there was this tremendously exciting new film about the Train Robbers. What was it called? *Buster*? Starring that man . . . er . . .

"By the way, what's the name of this actor chap we're going to see?" he asked, easing the zip upwards, just beneath Diana's creamy shoulder blades.

Diana laughed. "Phil Collins, silly. Don't you remember, we had him round for dinner the night Bunty let off the thunderflash and brought out the SAS?"

Charles searched his memory, and dimly recalled the night in question. But there had been so many. This would be one night at least where they would not end the evening with the likes of Ricketson-Smythe, Georgie Cavendish and the appalling Bunty Coker.

"He's a megastar, dopey. We've got all his CDs. We're bound to meet him after."

Diana brushed a speck of dust from his velvet collar. As she spoke, there came a discreet tap at the bedroom door and the figure of Sir Alan Fitztightly eased his way into the Royal Bedchamber.

"Ahem!" he coughed. "This has come, Sir." He proffered a silver salver to Charles on which lay an envelope with the words "Charlie and Di" in a boyish scrawl.

"Oh read it out, Fitztightly, do. We're late enough as it is."

Sir Alan tore open the envelope and, with a pained expression, began to read in a strangulated voice:

"Look, Your Highnesses. My advisers and me have thought about it and reckon it's not worth the hassle of you showing up. It could look as if you're in favour of, you know, GBH, and, let's face it, it's bad for you, it's bad for us, it's bad for business. However, we're biking round a little appreciation of what might have been. Be in touch. Take care. Ciao. Phil."

It took some seconds for Mr Collins's missive to sink in.

"Oh, hell!" Diana pouted, and threw her Zina Garrison designer handbag out of the window.

"Steady on, old girl." Charles tried desperately to console his wife, who had stomped into a corner and was staring petulantly out at the bright lights of the West End twinkling beckoningly across the park. Only seconds ago they had held so much promise. Now they merely mocked her.

"I mean, he's probably right. The papers would only blow it all up."

Charles moved towards his wife and offered a conciliatory arm. Her disappointment was obvious, and he wanted more than ever to find words to help . . . How had his old friend and mentor Sir Laurens van der Post summed it up?

"When there is no rice in the bowl, we must open a tin of baked beans." How very true. And what were the beans of the metaphor to be tonight?

"I know, darling. Why don't we play that new game, Trivial Pursuit? Sir Alan's awfully good at Art and Literature?"

A can of Timbella aersol-free hairspray hit him smartly on the of side the head . . .

T HEY HAD been sitting in near-silence for an hour when there was a screech of several powerful cars drawing up outside the front door. Footsteps pounded down the corridor and the sound of excited laughter could be heard drawing nearer.

Charles was deep in concentration as he put a small pink cheese into his container and moved three places round the board. Who was Frank Sinatra? he wondered. He had heard the name somewhere. And what was that noise?

In answer to his question, the oak-panelled doors burst open and in poured the unmistakable figures of Charlie, Bunty and Georgie, the latter wheeling a supermarket trolley filled to the brim with bottles of Safeways own-brand sparkling Mantovani.

"Surprise!" they all shouted. "Guess what we've got?"

Ricketson-Smythe was already fiddling with the video.

"I thought you lot were at the premiere with Phil!" exclaimed a delighted Diana.

"If Mahomet won't go to the movies," quipped Ricketson-Smythe, pressing the ON button, "the movies will have to come to Mahomet."

They all cheered and, as Bunty dimmed the lights and Georgie popped a cork, the screen burst into life with masked gangsters beating up an old train driver.

Charles began slowly to put away the box of questions. There were so many that he couldn't answer . . .

Chapter Thirteen

Prince Charles is due to address Britain's leading film makers at the opening of a new museum . . .

THE TRAFFIC crossing Waterloo Bridge was unusually heavy. Charles looked at his Louganis chronometer. Would he be in time for his important speech at the Melvyn Bragg Museum of the South Bank Show?

He thought over again about what he would say . . . Television - yes, it was a fantastically influential medium. And video - yes, that was a sort of new thing . . . it was shaping up nicely. Best to leave it impromptu for these sort of chaps, actors and so forth, they would not be expecting anything too scholarly.

"Ahem!" The chauffeur, Whittam-Smith, coughed. "Looks like a right snarl-up, Sir. I'll put something on the in-car entertainment, Sir, to while away the ensuing delay." Without waiting for a response, the rubicund driver merrily fiddled with the switches. The small television screen in the back next to the cocktail cabinet sprang into life.

How annoying, Charles thought. Silence was so important to one when one had one's thoughts to collect about one. As his friend and mentor Sir Laurens van der Post had once put it: "Only in the sea of silence can we find the fish of peace." How very true that was.

But now in front of his eyes flickered a kaleidoscope of ugliness. Large men with machine guns were firing out of helicopters, villages were being blown up, women raped. It was quite appalling. How had it got into his car?

He banged on the glass. "Whittam-Smith!" he exclaimed. "Where did you get hold of this horrid stuff?"

"It's one of Her Royal Highness's, Sir. I think Mr Coker brought this particular one in. *Killing Fields of Death III*. Hot stuff, eh?"

CHARLES smiled and took another sip of Old Mother Stoddard's Breakfast Tea. Yes, it had gone terribly well, though he said so himself. Just look at the headlines!

"Charles Slams TV Nasties," said *The Times*. "Prince Socks It To The Violent Video Bosses," echoed the *Daily Telegraph*. "Renewed Demonstrations In Nagorny Karabakh" screamed the *Independent*. And on every page his words rang out as a trumpet call for truth and decency. He read them aloud to Diana, who was listening to Phil Collins's *Groovy Kind of Love* on her dayglo Sports Walkman.

Not even this could dent his present feeling of wellbeing and achievement. If she would not listen, then there were others who would, people who understood his message for the media better than she.

"If anyone wants me," he said, getting up from the table, "I'm going to see a theatrical producer friend of mine."

CHARLES walked briskly up the narrow flight of stairs to his brother's office, marked by some curious theatrical tradition with the sign "Teaboy".

How he was looking forward to sharing his new-found insights with his impressionable younger brother! They were both communicators, after all, both with tremendous communications to communicate. But as he reached the half-open door Charles heard the distinctive tones of his brother.

"Delighted you've found time to see me, Mr Winner. I've seen all your films and, if I may say so, I think *Deathwish IV* is a masterpiece."

"I'm flattered to hear you say that, Eddie, my boy. And, with all due respect, you've got a lot more sense than that creepy brother of yours. He doesn't half talk crap, Your Majesty, with all due respect."

Edward laughed nervously. "Ha ha ha ha! Erm. . . you didn't have a chance to look through my synopsis, did you, Mr Winner? *Nightmare in Balmoral?*"

Charles peered round the door in disbelief, to see the figure of his brother, obscured by cigar smoke, pouring a mug of tea for the celebrated film director.

"Yeah, there are some great moments, Eddie, but it needs some work. You'd have to get more blood upfront to hook the punters."

Edward chimed in. "Yes, that's exactly what I thought. Great . . . Great . . ."

Charles could hardly believe his ears. Was this really the sensitive Edward who had abandoned the world of war for the nobler arts of the stage and screen?

The ruddy-faced impresario waved his cigar and continued: "Your brother is orf 'is bleedin' rocker, with all due respect. Nice cup of tea, this."

So the conversation continued - mocking, cynical and unfeeling. Suddenly Charles was seized with an overpowering desire to - how would they put it? - blow them away in a hail of lead . . . Bang, bang, bang . . .

Chapter Fourteen

Charles has been asked by the BBC to record a programme about modern architecture . . .

"QUIET, everyone! Let's go for another take. Ready, Your Maj?" The director stood precariously on the edge of the barge as it glided down the Thames. From his position in the prow, Charles could already see the famous skyline of the City. "It really is tremendously appalling . . ."

"Hold it! Wait till I say 'Action'!" The man in the pink sweater was getting impatient.

"And . . . action!"

"Oh, I do it now, do I?"

There was a stifled moan from the technicians, and even Dr Christopher Barkworth, the Prince's distinguished architectural adviser, irritably removed his spectacles and pretended to study the *Daily Telegraph* crossword puzzle.

Charles blushed. It was all proving more difficult than he had imagined.

"From the top. Take 10!" someone shouted.

"It really is tremendously appalling, the way this beautiful vista, so steeped in the work of Wren, Hawksmoor and other folk of that generation, has been disfigured by what can only be described as monstrous carbuncles like this shocking Esso Tower."

Charles smiled at having completed the opening paragraph of his speech without a mistake, and pointed dramatically at the skyline.

Unfortunately the barge was at that moment passing by St Paul's - a fact that Dr Barkworth felt obliged to point out.

"Er, Your Royal Highness, if I may say so," the bespectacled conservationist guru began, "that building is considered by most people to be St Paul's . . ."

"Oh, blow! It is so terribly difficult to coordinate this gesture and looking into the camera stuff."

As the barge laboriously turned a half-circle, ready for another run, Charles stared disconsolately at the eddying waters.

"There's so much litter, isn't there? Couldn't we bring it in somehow when I've done the carbuncle thing?"

The man in the pink sweater smiled through gritted teeth.

"What a brilliant idea, Sir! Jackie, make a note of that. Litter. Great!"

Despite the crew's obvious enthusiasm, Charles was nevertheless beginning to feel increasingly despondent about his inability to, sort of, come across. Thank goodness Diana and her friends were not there to see him. He must master this technology, he must tap his inner serenity. How had his friend and mentor Sir Laurens van der Post, himself a master of the medium, put it?

"The primitive man believes the camera steals the soul. The secret is to give it willingly."

How very true that was! The camera would be his friend. This time he would be word-perfect.

"It really is tremendously appalling, the way buildings like this St Paul's Tower . . ."

His words were drowned by the hooting of horns from a pleasure boat that had drawn up alongside the BBC launch.

"Yoo-hoo! Charlie!"

Charles turned to see a row of familiar faces leering over the rail of the pleasure cruiser *The Dockland Belle*. The passengers were

holding balloons and shaking up cans of lager, which they discharged in the direction of the film crew.

"Just came to see how you were doing. We thought you might need an audience. Ha ha ha!"

Charles groaned inwardly. It was them. Diana, wearing an off-the-shoulder nautical creation by Issi Gonis; Bunty Coker in fluorescent yellow braces; and Ricketson-Smythe gallantly holding up the recumbent figure of Georgie Cavendish, clutching an empty bottle of Old Hurd's Countryside Rum . . .

"It's a wrap. We'll go again after lunch."

"I'LL JUST turn off the lights. It'll be on any minute." Charles had been waiting for months to see his finished documentary, *The Future of British Architecture. Whither Are We Going?* And now here it was. 12.30 am. "A very good slot," the charming Mr Botney from the BBC had assured him.

"You'd be surprised at the figures for this time of night," he had said. "The *Blind Date* crowd will have just woken up again."

What had he meant by that? Charles edged his Rusbridger armchair forward. His mother coughed and patted the corgi, Sir Alastair.

The gentle strains of Arlott's London Sifonia filled the room and suddenly there he was, sailing majestically down the river. And there was Dr Barkworth nodding in polite agreement as he singled out the National Theatre and cried: "Just look at that. It really is appalling!"

And now there he was at Highgrove in his dove-grey Quinlan Terry suit, poring over the plans for the new Moroccan extension to his walled garden designed by Sir Gawayne Stamp.

"Look, Mama, look. There in the background - there's your old horse, Whitelaw!"

He turned to his mother and was taken aback to see her jaw dropped and hear the sound of light snoring emanating from the Royal Mouth.

"Really, Pater, Mother's gone to sleep in the middle of my documentary. It really is . . ."

But there came no reply from the Duke. Was it possible? Yes, he too had succumbed to a deep sleep.

Charles turned off the television and watched the small dot disappear into the centre of the screen. He wished that he too could disappear so easily . . .

Chapter Fifteen

The Princess of Wales has been asked to make a speech to Dr Barnardo's and to unveil its exciting new logo . . .

AN UNNATURAL silence hung over Kensington Palace. Walking discreetly past Diana's door, Charles was surprised and even a little unnerved not to hear the familiar thump of his wife's collection of Bros CDs. Was she ill? There had been a lot of 'flu around. Dr Barkworth, his distinguished architectural adviser, had gone down with a bad dose after falling into the Thames during the making of Charles's controversial documentary *It Really Is Appalling*.

Charles knocked tentatively on the door of the room marked "Di's Den", adorned with a bright yellow smiley face.

"Yah? Oh, hello, Charles. Can't talk now. I'm really, really busy with this speech."

Charles hovered uncertainly as he watched her sitting at her Massingberd Regency escritoire, surrounded by screwed-up pieces of paper. She was sucking a "BAD Tour" biro and was thumbing intensely through a book called *How To Speak In Public* by Gyles Brandreth and Nigel Rees.

Charles brightened. How wonderful! She was really taking this Barnardo's thing seriously. And how attractive she looked, so pensive. If only Fergiana and her ghastly friends could see the transformation.

"Can I help at all?" he inquired solicitously. "I do a bit of this public speaking thing myself - a few hints, perhaps?"

"Sweet of you, but really I can manage, thanks."

"I'll leave you in peace, then. You know where I am."

Of course, she wanted to do this herself. Closing the door softly, Charles tiptoed away down the corridor. After all these years there were genuine signs that she was turning away from her frivolous life towards a more mature role as his wife.

What was it his old friend and mentor had said all those evenings ago as they strode along the shingle towards The Lighthouse? "If you have patience, even the ostrich may one day spread its wings and fly." How very true that was! It was terrifically exciting the way she had sort of changed tack and come round to his way of, as it were, looking at things.

Back in his studio, Charles picked up his paintbrush and applied himself with new vigour to his watercolour, *The Inner City Sunset*.

THE applause was deafening. It was a standing ovation. From the platform Diana flushed pink with pleasure as two thousand matrons rose to their feet as one man to acclaim her brilliant and deeply moving defence of family life.

It was amazing! The cheering echoed through the vaulted Polly Toynbee Hall. As Diana sat down, the dynamic new president of Barnardo's (now "Kid Care"), Mr Justin Tierack, walked to the podium.

Sitting at home watching it all on the television, Charles felt an overwhelming sense of pride in his young wife.

Mr Tierack began: "Your Royal Graciousness. On behalf of everyone here, may I thank you for a truly magnificent speech."

As the cameras flashed and the pressmen surged forward, he continued: "Dare I suggest, Your Royal Ma'am, with the greatest possible respect, that your husband may well have to call on *your* services for his next effort?"

There was a roar of laughter, and renewed applause broke out spontaneously, in which Diana heartily joined.

Charles felt a sudden chill. There had been no applause for *his* recent "Video Violence" speech to the Institute of Video Nasty Producers, just barely concealed contempt. It was all very well for Diana to make occasional forays into the public domain, but the really serious issues were very much things that should be left to him - "the

thinking prince", as Sir Anthony Hillmore, the royal biographer, had once described him.

From the television came wave after wave of applause. And then, as the camera panned around the audience, he spotted three familiar figures. Surely it couldn't be them? But it was. They were soberly dressed in dark suits and spotted ties: Ricketson-Smythe, Coker, and Georgie Cavendish in an enormous flowered hat yelling "Encore!"

Sometimes, Charles thought, somewhat uncomfortably, as his eye caught the discarded Walkman on the floor next to the television, there was a case for one sticking to what one was really cut out for . . .

Chapter Sixteen

Charles's television programme It Really Is Appalling *has been acclaimed by the entire nation . . .*

CHARLES nodded his head vigorously in agreement as he sat in the darkened study of his Highgrove home. On the TV screen was the now-familiar picture of himself on a barge with Dr Barkworth, his architectural adviser, sailing down the Thames.

"I mean, look at this one!" he saw himself saying to the acquiescent Dr Barkworth. "It's like building a giant dustbin in the middle of a rosebed." How very true that was! And he had just thought of the analogy on the spur of the moment. And there was Dr Barkworth in complete agreement.

"How very true, Your Highness," concurred the bespectacled expert. "Dustbin in a rosebush. Frightfully good, Sir."

The more Charles viewed the video on his Japanese Edi Sha Remote Visotron V79 (another present from Emperor Hirohito), the better his performance appeared.

Yes, that was another good point when he told the American architect Hiram di Chirico that his new skyscraper was nothing more than "a huge pencil dwarfing humanity in its arrogance".

Quite a lot of the press had picked up on that one, actually. Even Diana had seemed to be impressed when he had read it out to her over a working brunch at which they had both been busy on new speeches about things that really matter. These days he felt a real sense of them being a team.

"You can use the pencil idea in your safe toys speech," he had said benevolently.

"Yah. Yah. Sure," Diana had agreed, thoughtfully chewing her "Save Great Ormond Street" felt-tip pen.

As the programme ended with the stirring strains of *The March of the Elizabethans* by Sir Howard Jacobsen, a knock at the door heralded the arrival of the top community architect from Belgium, Jean de Walloon, carrying a large cardboard box.

"Bonjour, Your Majesté," said the sprightly bow-tied figure sporting a neatly trimmed beard and thick tortoiseshell spectacles. "I have just been talking to your lovely wife. How interested she is in our project! So many good ideas!"

Yes, thought Charles, it was true. She was tremendously involved in such a real way.

Monsieur Walloon opened the box and with deft fingers assembled the model of Port Poldark which was that very minute being constructed on the coastal site in the middle of Charles's Cornish Duchy.

"You will see, Your Majesté. Everything low-rise. All local materials. Everything in harmony - the houses, the shops, the school, the church. Everything, how you say . . ."

The Belgian was momentarily lost for words. Yes, thought Charles, how would he say it?

A phrase of his old friend and mentor Laurens van der Post sprang unprompted to his mind: "No matter how high a man builds the roof, there is still earth under his feet." How very true that was, how very . . .

He was interrupted by the Belgian, who had lit a large Flemish pipe stuffed with aromatic Handelsman Dutch Navy Tartan Shag.

"I look forward so much to your visit and showing you Port Poldark in all its natural glory . . ."

A S THE Royal Party wended its way across the site, the pale November sun shed its sharp rays through the yellowing leaves and lit up the bright granite facings of the village. Everywhere there were local craftsmen, hard at work fashioning stone and trimming slate as their ancestors had done for centuries.

"Good morning, Your Majesty!" cried one such soul, wearing sandals, a smock and a long flowing beard. " 'Tis good to feel stone rising on stone once more. God bless ye, Sire!"

They moved on through the cobbled Trelawney Court, past the village cross and the old well, to where six proud dray horses were tethered to the wooden railings outside The Prince of Wales Arms, timber-framed and weatherboarded in traditional style.

"Look, darling!"

He turned to address his wife, who was walking behind him with the dapper Belgian. "See how perfectly the amenity area blends in with the municipal functions. No ugly cables and things. Everything's hidden, thanks to Mr Walloon's brilliant er concept. Hello, what's this?"

They had rounded the corner of Betjeman's Walk, to be confronted with a glaring pink neon sign that read: "Di's Smugglers' Discove".

"My God, that really is appalling!"

Charles hurried towards the gloomy entrance from which the dull thud of the Acid House track *Jack Your Body* clearly emanated.

He looked at his plans in disbelief.

"Walloon, what's the meaning of this? Dr Barkworth would have a fit. Where's the harmony in this?"

Walloon shrugged. "Is something wrong, Your Majesté? Is it not right?" He turned to the Princess. "But this is what you asked for, non? Ze community disco?"

"Dead right. Charles." She looked defiantly at her husband. "It's what ordinary people want. Like you said on your programme."

Walloon smiled. "People want to be happy. They dance. They sing. They are at one with the universe."

"Relax. Be happy!" thundered the music as Walloon took Diana's arm and led her merrily down the granite stairs . . .

46

Chapter Seventeen

Charles is celebrating his fortieth birthday. It is a day of national rejoicing. Or is it?

"IT REALLY is appalling," Charles began, as he threw down a copy of the *Sunday Times* with its screaming headline "Charles the Unhappy Loony - by Royal Biographer Anthony Hamlyn". He addressed his equerry, the sympathetic Sir Alan Fitztightly, who was laying out his best grey suit and burgundy tie, which Charles would wear at his "Young People's Party" in Birmingham.

"I mean, just listen to this!" Charles continued in a voice trembling with anger. " 'He is almost twice her age. No wonder they have nothing in common. He talks to plants whilst she boogie-woogies the night away.' I mean, I've never even met the chap. It really is appalling . . ."

"Quite so, Sir," concurred Sir Alan, putting a razor-sharp crease into Charles's grey westland trousers. "Perhaps I could drop a word in the ears of one or two of our friends in Fleet Street."

"You mean Dr Barkworth at the *Telegraph*?" asked Charles with a ray of hope that was soon stifled by the gloomy thought that it was not just the newspapers. "This Hamlyn chap is everywhere."

"Indeed he is, Sir," soothed Fitztightly, brushing a speck of dust from Charles's collar and spraying him with a little Benazir's Casbah Fragrance For Men - a birthday present from Major Ferguson that had arrived only that morning with a card saying "Spray this on, Charlie-boy, and the crumpet will come running!"

"Hamlyn was even on the television the other night, Sir. Same old tittle-tattle, I'm afraid."

"Yes. For two whole hours! Even longer than my own programme! It really is . . ."

"I know, Sir. Appalling."

Charles looked at himself in the mirror. A well-preserved 40-year-old of intelligent mien not, as Hamlyn would have it, some long-haired hippy chap in a loincloth. The bell rang.

"That'll be Whittam-Smith with the car, if I'm not mistaken, Sir . . ."

THE PARTY was in full swing. In the tramshed so lovingly restored by his loyal architectural adviser Ron Hackney, balloons floated from the ceiling, coloured lights flashed, and the Caribbean rhythms of Ozzy Buco and His Calypso Yardies throbbed as hundreds of young people gyrated in a joyous throng.

Charles moved among them; shaking hands with one, making jokes with another. Here was the dreadlocked figure of Solomon Rushdie who, with the help of the Prince's Trust, had started an organic T-shirt factory in Solihull.

"Happen I'm prospering, guv, thanks to your good self. Power to the Palace!"

"Splendid. Good man. Well done." Charles patted him on the back, almost dislodging the scented cigarette that his beneficiary was puffing.

And wasn't that Fatima Wondulu, who was now turning over £1 million a week with her takeaway herbal cushion business?

He felt a warm glow overtake him as he passed among his smiling subjects. How had his old friend and mentor Sir Laurens van der Post put it, as they had strolled together along Foster's Rock in the harsh outback of New South Wales?

"Even the humble thistle may produce a flower of perfect beauty. It is up to the gardener."

How very true that was! How very, very true!

"Wanna dance, Our Prince?" The bright Scouse accent of Tracy Farouk, proprietor of a Toxteth halal vegetarian cafeteria, interrupted his thoughts and, without waiting for an answer, the sari-clad single mother dragged him into the swirling band of dancers. Charles felt the pulsating rhythms of "The Three Wapshotts" course through his veins as he clapped his hands high above his head.

"You're a great little mover, Your Highness, even though you're as old as me dad," she beamed.

"When you're in lurv, you are in lurv," sang Stod Stoddy, the lead singer, and Charles sang along with him.

He was exhilarated. He felt young and vigorous. How had that song gone? "I could have danced all afternoon . . ." Well, something like that, anyway.

He wanted the music to go on and on. These people understood him. Not for them the sleazy tittle-tattle of the metropolis and Anthony Hamlyn's hurtful fictions. How wrong Hamlyn had been when he described him as "a middle-aged fogey sitting alone fiddling with his cello"! If Hamlyn could see him now he would have to eat his words!

Just then a young Afro-Cuban tapped him on the shoulder.

"Saw you on the telly the other night, chatting to that Hamlyn bloke. Great programme about your wife and all that."

"Yeah, I saw it too," chimed in an oriental teenager in faded jeans. "I wouldn't worry about it. You'll get over her. Probably find someone more your own age. Life's too short to worry, that's what I say!"

Suddenly the music stopped. The dancers drifted away. The strobe lights dimmed. Charles found himself standing alone by the Lilt dispenser.

"Out of order" it read. Yes, somehow he knew how the battered old machine felt . . .

Chapter Eighteen

Prince Charles has been out shooting with his father . . .

"**4092** BRACE! Pretty good for a day's bag, eh, boy?" boomed the Duke as he kicked open the door of the gunroom at Sandringham and handed his Rampling 12-bore to his faithful game-keeper Wapshott. "What was your haul?"

Charles followed his father into the room and stared gloomily out of the leaded window at the dusk falling on the ancient beech trees, already hoary with the evening frost.

"I . . . er . . . didn't have a very good . . . er . . . day," Charles said limply.

"Not surprised," replied the Duke, wrenching off his green Steadman boots and hurling them into the corner.

"I expect your mind was on other things, as usual. Bloody architecture, I shouldn't wonder. You can't spend your life mooning about over old buildings."

Charles listened unhappily as the Duke began to pluck the feathers from a seagull.

"That programme of yours was a nine-day wonder. Everyone's forgotten about it already."

A pale orange sun sank behind the bleak Norfolk wolds. Charles watched as the pile of white feathers at the Duke's feet grew bigger. As usual his father, in his gruff nautical way, had succeeded in exposing a raw nerve. Perhaps it was true?

Discreetly, Sir Alan Fitztightly slid into the room carrying a Barlow Claus handheld cellular phone. "Sir Gordon Giles for you, Sir. Will you be speaking to him?"

Charles brightened at the name of the celebrated literary agent from Giles & Giles who had some years earlier helped to publish his fairy story, *The Grand Old Loon of the Loo*.

"I'll take it in my office, if it's not too much trouble," he replied, sensing his father's disapproval.

"Literary johnny, is it? I despair of you sometimes, boy." The Duke turned away and began to saw the head off the seagull with a Swiss Navy hunting knife.

"GOOD NEWS, Sir." The well-modulated Edinburgh accent of London's most famous agent purred down the line. Charles felt his heart in his mouth. There had been talk of a book of the TV programme. Could this be it?

"I have received a very favourable offer indeed," continued the shrewd Caledonian. "From Messrs Hamish & Hamish - a very reputable firm, Sir, who suggested that you might like to adapt your highly acclaimed television programme into book form."

Charles was speechless.

"That's tremendous . . . How exciting! But I'm not really a sort of writer - more of a sort of, you know, front-chap . . ."

Sir Giles interrupted. "Ha ha ha! Far too modest, Sir, if I may say so. Sir Christopher Hamish himself proposes to edit the book and he describes your literary style as naturally gifted."

"Er . . . er . . . well . . . good grief . . ."

"An opinion, Sir," interposed Sir Giles with a voice as smooth as honey, "that I share. We were thinking perhaps of a title?"

As his agent spoke, Charles picked up the video cassette marked, in bold felt-tip, "BBC 1988: It Really Is Appalling" that was lying on his eighteenth century Rusbridger desk.

"I know. Why don't we call it . . . *It Really Is Appalling*?"

There was a gasp of astonishment at the other end of the line. "Positively brilliant, Sir. I can see it now at the top of the bestseller lists. Perhaps you could call in at our humble office to spare a minute to look through the contract. That's if it's no trouble, Sir. Ha ha ha!"

CHARLES climbed the rickety stairs of the Dickensian building in Old Frogmore Street in which the offices of Giles & Giles had resided for two centuries. Row upon row of leatherbound volumes lined the walls, each one a testament to the lasting merit of the printed word. What was it his old friend and mentor Sir Laurens van der Post, himself a great author, had said?

"A book is like a star. It shines for ever in the firmament of knowledge." How true that was. How very, very true.

And now his own book, his own thoughts and words, which had seemed so ephemeral when he spoke them to Dr Barkworth on the television as they travelled up the Thames, would now be sort of enshrined for ever, as it were. It made one feel tremendously humble.

Sir Gordon's door was half-open as Charles reached the top of the stairs. He could hear the clearly articulated tones of the canny Scottish man of letters speaking to someone on the telephone. Charles waited politely, eager to discuss his work.

"Look, Christopher, I know it's no bloody good, but it'll have his

photo on the front, hopefully with his wife - she sells magazines by the thousand. Anyway, we'll fill it full of colour pictures, keep the text down to a few captions, and sell it for Christmas '89. It'll walk out of the shops. We'll clean up, laddie!"

Charles paused, paralysed, his hand on the brass handle of the door. So that was how it was: his star destined to twinkle only briefly and then burn out . . .

Chapter Nineteen

A New Year dawns and with it new hopes for the future . . .

CHARLES was enjoying a late start to the day at Highgrove Park. Still wearing his Sidgwick & Jackson silk dressing gown, a present from Sir Anthony Blunt, he felt an unusual sense of pleasure as he rearranged his first editions of the works of his friend and mentor, Sir Laurens van der Post.

He caressed the spines of the familiar volumes. How many times he had perused them in search of some comforting aphorism: *Four Years in the Bush, My Jungle Safari, The Kernel of Truth, Pebbles on My Beach*. He pulled out the last of these and opened it at random.

"This is amazing, Diana," Charles said. "Listen to this."

Diana looked up from her newspaper. "Yah," she said perfunctorily.

" *'On the walls of a ruined Shinto Temple on the slopes of Mount Takeshita are inscribed these words:* Today's sun is yesterday's sun. Today's hopes are tomorrow's dreams.' "

He closed the book and clutched it to his chest. "That's incredible. A sort of synchronicity thing . . . what I was . . . er . . . sort of thinking myself . . ."

"Yah. But what about this? This is really interesting." Diana held up the front page of the *Telegraph* which had been mistakenly delivered by Sir Alan Fitztightly in place of her usual *Daily Mail*.

Charles crossed the room, his bare feet painfully picking up needles left over from the Christmas tree.

He looked over her shoulder at the dramatic headline: "Charlie Is Me Darling - Your Verdict".

There was no mistaking the *Telegraph*'s opinion poll. It showed that a huge majority had declared him the Most Popular Royal. Charles was momentarily stunned.

"That's fantastic. I had no idea. I mean, one tries, of course - architecture, inner cities, that sort of thing - but it's wonderful to think that one's sort of getting through. It makes one feel, I don't know, humble I suppose . . ."

Charles blushed with pleasure. Diana removed the Walkman

from her ears and laid it, still playing *Kylie Minogue's Greatest Hits*, on the arm of the leather Muggeridge sofa.

"Yah. And it says you should be King as well. High time your mother retired, that's what the people are saying."

Charles's response was immediate. "Are they really?"

Diana checked the seam of her stocking and then tore the ring-pull from a can of One-Cal Dr Stoppard's Diet Coke. "Read it for yourself."

Charles hungrily reread the article and saw that what Diana had said was true. All those myriad people out there really deeply felt that he, Charles, should be King.

"But, you know, she'll never go," he sighed.

Diana turned and fixed him with a steely glare. "How do you know? I bet you've never even asked her."

"Well, I mean, there's no need. I know what she'd say."

"Let's face it, Charles. You haven't got the guts. You're scared of her and you always have been."

"No. No. It's not like that at all . . . It's . . . er . . . it's er . . ."

T HE LATE afternoon sun caught the topmost turret of Windsor Castle and the Royal Standard fluttering in the unusually mild January breeze.

"Hello, Charles. What are you doing here? I thought you'd gone off skiing in Weidenfeld."

The Queen, dressed in tartan skirt and green Barbour jacket, bent down to pat the head of Sir Alastair, one of a throng of corgis waiting patiently for their daily ration of Sir Richard Body's organic "Corgo Chunks" and Runcie's Wholemeal Mixer.

"But since you're here you can help me feed this lot." She thrust an evil-smelling bucket of moistened dog biscuit into his hand and gestured to a row of bowls by the kennel doors. He knew the names off by heart: Sir Alastair, Massingberd, Rose, Dimbleby, Stevas . . . how he hated them all, with their sharp little barks and short tempers!

"Mother, I actually came to talk to you about something rather important," Charles ventured.

The Queen was engrossed in mixing up another tub of Sir Richard's wholesome feed.

"I don't know if you saw this thing in the paper . . ." Charles began.

The Queen grimaced. "Don't tell me your father's been talking nonsense again. I sometimes wonder what I ever saw in him. Dimbleby, that's not your dish. Don't be greedy now. Sit!"

Charles gamely persevered as the small dog gave an angry snarl and sank its teeth into his ankle.

"This poll about, you know, me being King and er . . . aargh!" His sentence was cut short as Stevas and Massingberd bounded across the lawn to join in the fray.

Trying to compose himself, Charles continued above their barking.

"I just wondered if you ever thought of giving all this up and letting me have a go."

The Queen shook her head in disbelief. "I don't know who talks more rubbish, you or your father. I can't give all this up when it's obvious that the dogs don't even like you. Come here, Hamilton - I won't tell you again!"

Charles made one last desperate attempt to make his mother understand.

"Don't you think, in all honesty, mother, it might be time to go?"

The Queen plopped a scoop of Body-Mix into the last silver corgi bowl.

"You've only just arrived, but I suppose if you must, you must." She proffered her cheek dismissively to Charles and he obediently kissed her.

"And do shut the gate, dear. Last time Dimbleby got out the postman had to have his leg amputated."

THE VILLAGE clock was striking midnight when Charles got back to Highgrove. "Well, how did it go?" Diana put the video of *Poltergeist II* on Pause. "What did she say?"

Charles walked to the fire, conscious of his tattered trouser leg and bruised ankles.

"We had it all out and really talked it through - you know, heart to heart, and er . . ."

"So it was a big floppo, was it?"

"No. No."

Charles searched for ways to convince Diana of the success of his mission. "She's taking it all very seriously and I think there's real hope there. I mean, like Sir Laurens says, tomorrow's hopes are today's sunsets or whatever it is he says . . . er . . ."

Diana was not listening. She was back watching *Poltergeist* and the TV screen was filled with objects of furniture whirled around the room by an unseen force.

How very like his own life that seemed. How very . . .

Chapter Twenty

Diana has gone to the Caribbean to get away from it all . . .

"ENTER!" The unmistakable timbre of the Duke's nautical command summoned Charles through the oak-panelled door and into his father's dressing room. The Duke was supervising the packing of a large cabin trunk bearing the inscription "His Royal Highness Admiral of the Fleet the Duke Of Edinburgh" in preparation for the funeral of Emperor Hirohito in Japan.

Charles stood awkwardly, waiting for his father to begin the inevitable tirade. For on top of the trunk were displayed the centre pages of the nation's grubbiest tabloids, showing his young wife disporting herself in a flimsy Montefiore one-piece lycra clingsuit. "Yes, It's Nu-Di!" screamed *The Times* in typically tasteless fashion. "GEC Rejects Takeover Bid!" trumpeted the *Independent*.

The Duke opened the bottom drawer of the dressing table and produced a large ornamental sword, a present from the late King Zog of Albania.

"I thought we'd sorted this lot out!" he bellowed, thrashing the papers with the point of his weapon. The valet, ex-Chief Petty Officer St John Underwear, coughed discreetly and melted from the room.

Charles trembled as the Duke continued: "Look at her! No better than a Bangkok floozy plying for trade! She's your wife, damnit! Can you imagine your mother at that age prancing about the River Dee

in galoshes and a bikini?"

Charles searched desperately for some mitigating factors.

"Er, well, she needed a break. A lot of stress . . . you know . . . that sort of thing."

The harder Charles tried to explain, the flimsier his excuses sounded. At that point St John Underwear returned with a selection of hats including that of a colonel in the Greek Foreign Legion, the Teufel of the German Boy Scout movement, and the reinforced steel top hat of the Veteran Coach and Pair championship.

"Not those, you bloody fool! It's a funeral not a bloody picnic! Something for the slitty-eyed brigade!"

Charles knew he was at the point of no return. His father's rages knew no abating. As his friend and mentor, Sir Laurens van der Post, had put it: "When the hurricane engulfs the village, even the snail can find no shelter." How very true that was, he thought, as he sat perched on the Gorby trouser press, which was unfortunately still plugged in.

"And that won't be the only malarkey she's up to, believe you me," said the Duke, emptying a drawerful of assorted medals into the trunk.

"No . . . no," Charles remonstrated. "She's . . . er . . . with her mother."

"Yes. The divorcee. What kind of chaperone is that? A bolter, mark my words. You'd better do something, boy, before that wife of yours makes a laughing stock of us all!"

Charles turned and, as he did so, bumped into the cringing Underwear, who was dragging a large box of thigh-length black ceremonial boots marked "The property of Prince Albert" into the room.

C HARLES dialled the international code for Necker Island again. 010-417-7372837. The very name filled him with apprehension. The Duke had planted the seeds of doubt in his mind.

He had seen it only as an innocent trip abroad but was it possible that . . .? No, surely . . . he must be mistaken . . . Yet you did read about that sort of thing happening . . .

Brrr . . . Brr . . .

It was a very small island, surely someone must be at home . . .

And those pictures certainly were . . . well, phew . . . he loosened his collar slightly.

"Hi there, mateys. Branson here!" The jocular voice of the bearded condom entrepreneur and balloonist boomed over 4,000 miles. "I'm not picking up the phone at the moment but if it's Virgin business could you ring Steve or Gary at our London office and they'll get right on to it."

The recorded message was interrupted by the deep fruity tones of someone who was clearly a native.

"Dat you, José? Where da hell are that them grass, then?"

Charles tried to picture the island, but was confused. How could they need grass?

"I'm not José. I'm terribly sorry. This is Charles from England, well sort of England really or rather Wales."

The voice at the other end laughed. "Well, whatever you're on, fly some of it in pretty damn quick!"

"Look, can I speak to Mr Branson, or better still to my wife?"

"Mr Branson gone op in am balloon. All de rest am skinny-dippin' in de bay, stoned out dere brains if you ask me. You're not de press, are you?"

"No, this is a personal call. When they come back could you say Diana's husband rang?"

"I don't know when dere comin' back. Dey often out all night, relaxin' an' dat."

The voice broke into a calypso:

"All day, all night, Lady Di,

Down by de seashore, gettin' high . . ."

With a sinking heart Charles replaced the receiver softly in its cradle. Perhaps after all he should have gone to Hirohito's funeral. It would have been just the thing to cheer him up . . .

Chapter Twenty-one

Diana has been to a rehabilitation centre for young alcoholics, but she went alone . . .

THE ALARM on Charles's new digital MikiRuni wristwatch gave off a series of high-pitched bleeps, and the computerised oriental voice intoned: "It is nine o'crock, Your Highness, precisery."

"Good grief. It's time for the news."

Charles put down his brush and left the watercolour he had been working on, a view of the old melon market in Viraj Mendis in Udaipur. He paused briefly to admire the way the sky was taking shape . . . a sort of bluey blue, but the feeling of tremendous heat he remembered would be more difficult . . . how could one capture that sort of haze thingy? Perhaps he would ring Sir Hugh after the news.

He pointed the remote control device at the television and the picture sprang to life. It was a moment or two before the item he was waiting for appeared and, as the newscaster spoke solemnly about

outbreaks of food poisoning in supermarkets, Charles helped himself to another tumbler of Old Glenelton's Double Malt, a Christmas present from his favourite ghillie, Ben McWheatcroft.

And suddenly there she was! His wife Diana, radiant as ever, yet dressed more sensibly, he thought, in a sort of two-piece suit thing. Much more appropriate than those low-cut outfits his father got so bad-tempered about.

The newscaster described Diana's visit to the Dr Jeff Bernardo's Alcohol Abuse Clinic in Soho as "a triumph". Then the camera moved into close-up and she began to speak to the grizzled inmates.

"It really is appalling," she began in her soft but stilted tones, "how television and soap operas encourage young people to drink. They show them in pubs and wine bars and it sets a very bad example. It really is appalling."

The audience of journalists clapped appreciatively and the newscaster smiled as he put away his pen and shuffled his papers.

"The Princess of Wales in Soho today. And here are the main points of the news again. .."

Charles greeted the news item with satisfaction. Yes, she really was sort of making a real contribution as it were and taking a serious interest in serious things. It was a kind of growth experience. How had his old friend and mentor Sir Laurens van der Post put it in his book *The Sower and the Seed*?

"When the baby loses its rattle it soon learns to swim."

It was something like that, anyway. And whatever it was it was very, very true. Like everything the old boy said, it made tremendous sense even if you didn't quite remember what it was.

He helped himself to another couple of fingers of whisky and his eye was caught by the maxim printed in gold lettering on the label beneath the picture of an old kilted Scotsman standing by a frothing burn holding up a dead sheep: "Have one afore ye gang." How very true *that* was. It was not only Sir Laurens who had the gift of tongues. The old Caledonian too knew a thing or two about the inner voyage.

He felt a warmth come over him and he felt at one with the universe. Sometimes there were moments like that when everything fell into place. Diana . . . on the television, how wonderful . . . how sort of in control of everything . . . what was it she had said? "It really is appalling." A very good opening for a speech, that. He felt he had heard it before but never mind. . . Charles emptied the remains of the bottle into his glass and took a deep draught.

This was the perfect time to finish that picture. Perhaps he should forget the melons and put in an elephant or two. There must have been a couple around, perhaps flying over the rooftops. Yes!

He stood up but felt strangely tired. Maybe he would have a little nap before Diana came back. He must do something about that carpet. It really was appalling, the way it kept going round . . .

"DARLING. Wake up!" The voice seemed to be coming from down a long corridor. Then Charles opened his eyes and, in the dancing haze, saw the familiar features of his wife bending over him.

"What did you think? Wasn't I terrific?"

"Oh . . . yes . . . The speech, oh, it was . . . terrific . . . it was marvellous . . . let me get you a drink . . . we must celebrate . . . I'll get Sir Alan to open a bottle of champagne."

Why was she looking at him like that?

Chapter Twenty-two

Diana is about to leave for New York on a cultural visit . . .

"BUT DARLING, you've only just come back from the Caribbean. I mean, look, you're still tanned." Charles strode to the window and gazed out over the Highgrove Hills. A ray of warm sunshine penetrated the leaded windows and bathed his face in light. Outside, the cherry trees were already suffused in pink blossom in this warmest of warm winters and the birds sang merrily as their thoughts turned to nest-building.

Once again the annual miracle of nature stood poised like a kingfisher on a bough. How had his friend and mentor, Sir Laurens van der Post, described the changing season? "The white sheet of winter becomes the yellow duvet of spring."

Charles turned to his wife, who was placing her Sumo Walkman and a collection of her favourite T'Pau cassettes into an overnight bag.

"It seems such a pity you're going to New York when it's so marvellous here."

Diana unpeeled an "I Love New York" sticker and pressed it on her zebra-skin Annigoni holdall.

"Not that old record again, Charles. It's wearing rather thin."

Her tone surprised him and he felt as if he had been stung by a hornet. She continued: "I mean, you're away just as much as me."

Charles rose inevitably to the bait.

"Yes, but darling, my things are sort of work things . . . I mean, one doesn't enjoy them, they just have to be sort of done . . ."

Diana laughed mockingly as she rang the bell for Sir Alan Fitztightly to take her bags down to the car.

"Like your three months fishing at Balmoral last summer?" Her sensuous mouth curled into a cruel sneer.

Charles stiffened and raised his voice. "No, that's an environmental . . . er . . . you know . . . recharging of inner batteries . . . like Sir Laurens in Africa."

"Oh no, don't give me him again." Diana placed her hands on her hips and faced Charles. "I'm surprised you didn't marry *him*."

Startled, Charles stepped backwards just as Sir Alan discreetly entered the room, and crushed his equerry's slippered toe under his stout English Adam Smith brogues.

"Er . . . ouch, Sir!" Sir Alan coughed discreetly and hopped into the room. Diana pointed at the bags and Sir Alan whisked them up under his arm and shimmered, hobbling, from the room.

There was a heavy silence. Outside a stag bellowed to its mate in the sunshine.

Charles knew what he had to say: "Darling, don't let's quarrel. I know we've agreed to sort of do our own thing . . . I mean, you've got your things and I've got my . . . er . . . things. It really is appalling if we're going to spend all our time rowing."

"OK." Diana nodded. "It's not as if I'm going to New York just for a laugh. What with that opera and the visit to the Harlem AIDS clinic I'll hardly have time to see Bunty's friend Milo who runs Herpes on 7th and 54th. I mean, no one goes to New York without going *there*."

Charles had very little idea what his wife was talking about, but felt a strong need to say goodbye on a positive note.

"Yes, of course. Yes. And I've got plenty to do this end. My Spitalfields project is tremendously exciting and the Punjabi craft centre is coming on a treat . . ."

Charles followed down the corridor as his wife strode purposefully past portraits of her ancestors by Sir Joshua Nkomo and other members of his school. Diana stopped by a picture of herself mounted on her pony Ringo (the work of the late Sir Alfred Munnage RA) to check her passport.

Charles drew level. "I'm so glad we've talked this over sensibly. I think from now on we'll find everything much easier. I mean, this Big Apple . . . Enjoy! Isn't that what they say?"

But Diana was already in the Lonrho GTI, roaring away down the drive. He waved, but his view was obscured by the limping figure of Sir Alan, his foot swathed in a huge bandage, on crutches and supported by the ample frame of Charles's trusted housekeeper, Mrs Waldegrave.

"Easy does it, Sir Alan. We can't have you playing any physical sports for a month or two, can we?" She gave the luckless factotum a broad wink. Charles smiled at this homely scene. Life was not really so appalling, after all . . .

A T THREE o'clock that morning Charles was still tossing and turning. He eventually gave up the quest for sleep and stumbled downstairs. The house seemed large and empty, the darkness enveloped him like a cloak. Outside an owl hooted mournfully.

How could he fill the long night hours now he was once again on his own? He turned on the Te Kanawa Sky TV set, a gift from that kind American Mr Murdoch, and settled down gloomily to see if there was anything on the all-night news channel.

And there she was. More beautiful and more radiant than he had ever seen her, being swept down Fifth Avenue in the midst of a huge crowd of photographers.

The vast New York skyscrapers glinted in the sharp sunlight as she turned to a reporter.

"I just love New York," she told him. "I'm so happy here."

Chapter Twenty-three

Diana has been visiting the US to great acclaim from the delighted Americans. But she is not the only royal visitor this month . . .

"WHERE the hell d'you think you're going, bud?" The tall burly airport security officer put his hand menacingly on his gun and blocked Charles's route to the VIP arrival suite at New York's Leonard Bernstein airport.

"Er, I'm the Prince of Wales. I'm here on a sort of private visit. My wife was here last week." He blurted out his excuses nervously.

"Oh yeah?" queried the officer. Charles looked around apprehensively for his welcoming committee until his eye caught a hand-held sign with the words "Prince Charles" in crude felt-tip capitals on it being held aloft.

"Ah, I'm expected, you see. There's my man there."

A bespectacled, rather drab figure stepped forward.

"Welcome to America, Sir. Mr Chancellor, Under-Secretary to Sir George. He is so sorry he couldn't come, he had to go to the Tibetan exhibition. Your transport is waiting."

Charles shook the man warmly by the hand. "I quite understand. My decision to come was a bit of a spur of the moment thingy."

Chancellor nodded obsequiously. "If I may say so, Sir, your wife went down terribly well. They love that sort of thing over here."

Yes, thought Charles, they certainly did. But now it was up to him to demonstrate that there was more to royalty than parading around Fifth Avenue in the latest Galtieri designer clothes from Sikorski's. There was ecology, architecture, rainforests, the greenhouse heating-up syndrome that everyone was talking about. The Americans were very "into" that sort of thing as well.

Chancellor ushered him towards the airport bus, which displayed the route: "Newark - New Jersey - Hoboken Freeway - Dworkin - New Dworkin - Stringboot, Arizona - Whistling Arrow - Dodge City - Reno - Washington DC."

Chancellor again looked apologetic. "It really is much quicker by bus, Sir, and you get a much better view of the scenery."

Charles braced himself and sat down beside a huge Navajo Indian in traditional costume drinking bourbon from a bottle. Yes, this was the real America, he thought. Diana would not have seen anything like this.

The bus jolted into motion, dislodging a large 300lb bag of heroin from the roofrack which fell and caught him squarely on the head.

A Chinese voice behind him shouted: "Stop thief!" and had to be restrained by Mr Chancellor.

CHARLES had freshened up from his three-day coach journey and felt restored and invigorated by his travels. He had seen so much and met so many people - Rev Bonecrusher from Yumstown, Illinois; that extraordinary black woman who wrestled with snakes; and, perhaps most fascinating of all, the Jewish travel agent Yonty Lemsip, with his wealth of colourful stories about life on Mars.

It had all been so enlightening. How had his old friend and mentor, Sir Laurens van der Post, put it? "The traveller is a man who meets everyone but himself." How very true that was!

And now he was to meet Mr Bush, the most important American of all.

The door opened to a piped fanfare of "America The Beautiful" and in stepped a small dapper man in golf slacks.

"Hi there, Chuck! I'm sorry George couldn't be with us. He had to go bury an emperor. I'm Dan Quayle, VP of the US. I'm delighted to meet you, Sir. You and I have a lot in common. We both stand waiting in the wings, a heartbeat away from a decent job."

The tiny figure cackled and grabbed a putter from his desk.

"This is a par three to the wastepaper basket. Want a try?"

Charles coughed. "Not really my bag . . . I was hoping to look at some buildings . . . It's fascinating what some of your architects have been doing . . . We could learn so much."

"You wanna see some buildings? Look over there!" Quayle waved towards the floor-to-ceiling windows with his club, indicating a panorama of skyscrapers stretching to infinity. "We got millions of the damned things."

Charles tried to change the subject, to find some common ground with this young man who seemed so full of energy and life.

"And this ozone layer . . . I know all of you over here are very concerned about CFCs."

For a moment the vice-president looked puzzled. "Yeah sure, we've got the FBI on it right now." He tapped the ball confidently along the carpet.

Charles had the feeling that the meeting had not been a success. But then suddenly the American's face brightened. A sense of recognition spread across his handsome features.

"Say, I know what I meant to ask you. I've been dying to know one thing."

Charles breathed a sigh of relief. At last they were getting somewhere. Initial meetings were often awkward, but once you got to engage their interest the Americans really were very open and charming folk, keen to learn about things.

Quayle stepped closer to Charles and put his arm round his shoulders conspiratorially.

"Where did your wife get that swimming costume? Boy, she could have been on the cover of *Sports Illustrated* in that little number. And when I say little, I mean eeny-meeny-itsy-bitsy. Wow!"

He made a whooping noise and punched his fist in the air.

"Say, will you do me a favour, Chuck? Send me a signed photo of the lady. And send it to the office." He winked. "Mrs Quayle's a bit on the born-again side."

Charles walked morosely to the window and looked out at Arlington Cemetery. The eternal flame had gone out again.

Chapter Twenty-four

Charles has been invited to address a world conference on "Planet Earth" . . .

CHARLES had been in his study at Windsor Castle since dawn. His copious notes were spread out before him on the leather-topped Courvoisier escritoire. Outside it was an unusually mild March day, and he could see swathes of tulips from his vantage point at the top of the Sir Antoine de Blunt Tower. Tulips in full bloom, he thought, and it was still winter. It was worrying. He wrote down, furiously: "This greenhouse thing, ladies and gentlemen. It really is appalling." It was also very stuffy and Charles got up to open the tiny leaded window. At that precise moment a gust of wind blew into the room, scattering his papers all over the floor.

Charles bent down to pick up a sheet on which was written "CFC the threat. Tell joke about Cricklewood Football Club" when there came a knock at the door.

Charles was amazed to find his father entering tentatively, his normally stern expression softened into a benign smile.

"Hello, old boy, just popped into the crow's nest to see what's on the horizon. I say, this looks jolly interesting." He bent down and began collecting up the paper. "Let me give you a hand."

Charles was taken aback by his father's sudden interest in his work. Perhaps he was really getting through to him. The old could often learn from the young. What was it that his friend and mentor Sir Laurens van der Post had once told him?

"The ageing ostrich is led into new paths by the egg." How true that was when you sort of worked it out, how very, very true . . .

His father had put on his spectacles and was studying some cuttings from the *Guardian* intently. "I say, listen to this. 'By 2030 the acreage of rainforest left will be less than the size of Wales.'

Absolutely fascinating. Can I take this away and get it photocopied?"

Charles was delighted. This was a side of his father that he had never suspected before.

"By all means. And, er . . . there are some other things you might want to have a look at . . . this book here."

"What's this?" asked the Duke as Charles handed him a large leatherbound volume. *"The Last Rhinoceros of the Antarctic.* This van der Post chappie, you're rather fond of him, aren't you? Very sound, isn't he?"

Charles admitted that he had only read the introduction by Dr Christopher Barkworth but was sure there was a lot of first-class material that his father would really find sort of important.

The Duke finally left the room some hours later, his arms piled high with books, folders and newspaper clippings.

"Most enjoyable chinwag. Do it again some time," he called as he descended the narrow stone staircase.

Charles sighed with pleasure. You know, despite his manner the old fellow was really a pretty decent sort when you got to know him . . .

C HARLES was feeling a great sense of satisfaction. His warnings on the ozone layer had been a terrific success. Not since his TV programme *It Really Is Appalling* had there been such acclaim.

He had forgotten how little he had eaten during the composition of his speech and he was feeling hungry. Perhaps Mrs Waldegrave would give him something on a tray, perhaps a vegetable samoza or maybe a yoghurt sandwich? As he passed the green drawing room he could hear the sound of cheers and raised voices. He stopped to listen.

"Wasn't he wonderful?" his mother's regal tones boomed out. Several corgis yapped assent in the background. "Such a terrific speech and he spoke so fluently,"

He could hear Edward agreeing. "Yah, yah. Great perf. We could have him in one of our shows anytime. He'd be perfect for *Aspects*. They should put the whole thing to music."

His sister Anne concurred. "Well, he always has felt deeply about these things . . . the environment and all that." Even Diana joined the chorus of approval. "He's fab. A real shaker."

It was rather embarrassing. It would be better to tiptoe away really. But then the oak door swung open and his mother appeared, a glass of champagne in her hand.

"Oh, there you are, darling. You've just missed your father's splendid lecture on the television. We were all riveted. Come in and have a glass of champagne. We're all going to watch it again on the video device."

Charles limply accepted the Waterstone crystal goblet and took a sip of the Piper Gauleiter champagne. Was it only his imagination or had the sparkle already gone out of it?

Chapter Twenty-five

Charles and Diana have been invited to make a Royal visit to Saudi Arabia . . .

It was late afternoon and the sun's fierce heat was beginning to fade. The sands of the desert, timeless and mysterious, were cooling after the cruel blistering fire of the Middle Eastern day. Charles placed his shaving things carefully on a vast marble basin in the en suite bathroom of King Faht's Royal Suite in the Summer Palace at Jedi. He had been looking forward to this trip so much as a chance to explore at first hand the subtle and often misunderstood way of life of this remote Bedouin kingdom.

The simplicity of the tent-dwelling Whallis roaming the sandy wastes with little more than their camels, a few goats and their innate comprehension of their spiritual relationship to their unyielding surroundings. Yes! To stare heavenwards with only a humble carpet between one's head and the shifting dunes beneath, this was the stuff of his boyhood dreams.

How had his old friend and mentor Sir Laurens van der Post put it? "There is no water in the desert but there one drinks deep from the wells of life." How true that was, how very true . . .

But somehow so far it had not lived up to his expectations. The huge six door stretch Pamella Turbo XGI that had met them at the airport seemed a far cry from the anticipated camel ride. And although Diana had enjoyed the in-car video facility he would have preferred the comparative silence of the four lane German-built Autobahn across the Salman desert.

And their accommodation. He did not want to appear ungrateful to his host but the king-size marble sunken bed covered in black satin with overhead mirrors had surprised him.

Moreover, the inner serenity brought about by the abstinence from alcoholic beverages that Sir Laurens had described in his seminal book *The Lost Sandmen of Khashoggi* seemed somewhat at odds with the built-in-seven foot Westmoreland mini-bar, filled to the brim with of every conceivable type of spirit.

As Charles nearly fell into the olympic size jacuzzi he thought to himself: "It really is . . . well if not exactly appalling then certainly a bit sort of over the top."

Still, there was always the consolation that behind the opulent display remained the simplicities of the Berber code that placed such emphasis on the dignity of women. So unlike the permissive trend in the West where people had forgotten the virtues of chivalry and respect. His mind turned to a picture of his wife's friend Bunty Coker pulling down his trousers and "mooning" at Georgie Cavendish during the trooping of the colour. No, here he could rely on his hosts to maintain a strict decorum.

"Now let's run it through again, darling." Charles addressed Diana who was putting the final touches to her make-up.

"Do we have to? I know all that. That drippy little man from the FO gave me the etiquette book. I read it on the plane."

Charles raised an eyebrow. "I don't know. I thought Gore-Booth was rather a good chap. Steeped in Arab history and speaks all the languages. He read oriental studies at Peterhouse. Apparently it's very easy to offend these chaps."

Charles pulled out an official-looking memo from the pocket of his safari suit. "Rule No. 1. Ladies must never cross their legs at dinner."

"Yah. Yah. No probs. Where's my walkman? King Faht gave me a gold one at the airport . . ."

S O FAR the banquet seemed to be going without incident. The huge roast camel stuffed with Rolex watches borne in by twelve eunuchs had been not nearly as bad as he had feared and moreover was apparently organically reared. And these locusts fried in honey were really no worse than snails. It was far too easy to be dismissive about other people's mores.

He looked up to see his wife chatting happily to several of King Faht's sons who seemed greatly taken with Diana's conversation.

Even his own companion, Prince Avin Aziz, the King's uncle-in-law, was doing his best to communicate.

"In London, I have seen your Harrods and your Wigmore Street. Your Major Ron, what a tophole chap he is. A one for the ladies, yes?"

Charles did his best to steer the conversation back to the ozone layer and the deforestation of Arabia.

"If you go on like this, the whole place could soon become a desert", he found himself saying.

The bearded potentate popped a sheep's-eye thoughtfully into his mouth and looked uncomprehendingly at Charles.

"This watch," Prince Avin continued, stubbing a fat finger at the gem-encrusted timepiece on his wrist. "It cost me £6 million pounds in Cartier's. I sell you for little kiss of pretty wife."

Oh dear. Charles blushed. It was not progressing quite as well as he had hoped. Gore-Booth had not mentioned anything like this. Would it be a dreadful sort of snub to refuse the Arab's proposition?

Luckily the attention of everyone was suddenly shifted to events at the other end of the table where a loud shriek from one of the Bedouin princelings pierced the air, as he jumped clutching his hand which appeared to be pierced by a golden kebab skewer which only a second before had been in Diana's grasp.

The rest of the princelings were laughing. King Faht shouted down the table.

"Serve you right, Abdul. You keep your hands above the table when you sit next to the Princess. You're not in Mayfair now."

No, Charles thought, we are not. And for the first time part of him wished that they were . . .

Chapter Twenty-six

It is Christmas time at Windsor, and the family are gathered together as usual for their traditional Yuletide pursuits . . .

"LISTEN to this one!" Edward picked up the white slip of paper that had fallen from the Secker & Warburg cracker. "Why did the Major cross the road? To get to the Massage Club!"

"It doesn't say that!" bellowed the Duke, picking the bones of the roast barn owl from his teeth. "That's enough of that smut from you, boy."

"Read it out properly, Edward," intervened the Queen. Her youngest son groaned. "You read it, Charles."

Charles was miles away, thinking of how much he had enjoyed his televised trip up the Thames with Dr Barkworth . . .

"Sorry . . . er . . ."

"The motto, Charles. Do read it out," insisted the Queen, putting her plate on the floor for her beloved corgi Sir Alastair to lick clean.

Charles tried to join in the family badinage that always followed Mrs Hussey's excellent twelve-course luncheon.

"Er . . . The fool is no more than a wise man who knows he is foolish . . . Gosh, that's rather good."

"What's the joke? What's so funny about that?" barked the Duke.

"It's not a joke, it's a sort of thinking point, kind of aphorism . . ."

"Balderdash!" The Duke stood up, brushing feathers and Brussels sprout leaves from the front of his full-dress uniform, that of an admiral in the Coldstream Guards.

"Actually, Sir, it appears to be written by an old friend of mine, Sir Laurens van der Post . . ."

But the Duke was looking at his watch.

"Just time for a round of charades. I'll think of the titles - no cleverdick books, just good old films. We had *Born Free* last year."

"Yes, that was awfully good," said the Queen. "Edward played the lion with a mop on his head."

Anne, who had been silent until then, added: "Yes, and you shot him with a broomstick - which wasn't in the film at all."

"Right!" The Duke closed the curtains on the darkening landscape of Windsor Safari Park, where a few wildebeest huddled disconsolately together beneath the naked oak trees. "You, boy! Take your brother and sister upstairs to the nursery and get the props."

This last command was directed at Charles, and it brought back vivid memories of previous Christmases with their old rivalries and sibling arguments.

L ITTLE had changed in the tiny room at the top of the stairs. The pink rabbits on the wallpaper had faded, and the brass fender in the fireplace had not been polished since the days of Nanny Newman. And there in the corner was the battered school trunk that contained the dressing-up clothes. "P. Charles, Waldheim House, Gordonstoun" was painted on the outside in neat white capitals, now flaking with age.

How powerful the images of childhood remain, he thought. Almost like sort of ghosts; it was really quite eerie in a kind of weird Dickensian way. There they were, all those years ago, playing with Hornby trains on the carpet.

"Who would have thought, I mean, years ago," Charles ruminated, opening the trunk and picking up a lead Zulu warrior with one arm missing, "that we three who used to sort of perform shows for each other up here should end up as it were having such a role on television as we have?"

Edward plunged a rubber sword into his stomach and gave a gruesome howl.

"Yah. We're all in the biz . . ." He fell clumsily to the floor while Charles continued.

"I mean, you, Anne, you were terrifically good with that little Walden chap. So natural, so laid back."

Anne walked to the fireplace and ran a finger along it, picking up the dust.

"Nothing to it. If you are talking about a really important issue it's very easy."

"Yah. I found that with *It's A Knockout*," said Edward from behind a gorilla mask. "Everyone said it was really pro."

Charles went on: "You see, we're the first generation of Royal communicators on a giant scale. Millions of people saw my programme, and of course yours, but mine was really important in the sense that I could point to these buildings and say it really *is* appalling."

Edward donned a false nose and moustache. "'Fraid I missed your perf, bro'. I was up all night with the cast of *Phantom,* working in some new material I'd suggested."

"Ah," persisted Charles. "It's a pity you missed it because, although I say so myself, it was a great . . ."

The door swung open to reveal the imposing figure of Her Majesty the Queen, wearing a paper crown and holding the docile form of Sir Alastair under her arm.

"Come along, children! It's nearly three o'clock and I'm about to address 600 million people throughout the world. You three will be among them."

They descended the stairs to the living room as the strains of the national anthem began.

"Watch carefully," she said directly to Charles. "You might have to do this someday."

Charles meekly took his seat and was once again the little boy in a sailor suit watching the most popular TV show in the history of the world . . .

To be continued . . .